*To my wife, Rosemary, and my Aunt Es (RIP) –*
*for bringing simple clarity as well as profound*
*understanding to what daily life is all about.*

Published in 2014 by Ballpoint Press
4 Wyndham Park, Bray, Co Wicklow, Republic of Ireland.
Telephone: 00353 86 821 7631
Email: ballpointpress1@gmail.com
Web: www.ballpointpress.ie

ISBN 978-0-9926732-6-0

Book design and production by Elly Design

Printed and bound by GraphyCems

# Contents

# About The Author

PJ Cunningham is an author, journalist and publisher who was brought up on a small farm in Clara, Co Offaly but now lives in Bray, Co Wicklow.

His previous book about growing up in rural Ireland, *The Lie Of The Land*, was published last year. Before that in 2001, his book of short stories, *A. N. Other*, focused on rural life as seen through GAA activity in a parish.

Married to Rosemary O'Grady, they have five children.

# Preface

Like my last book – *The Lie Of The Land* – the tales in this collection straddle the chasm between the short-story genre and a collections of old tales.

The stories contained in *The Long Acre* focus on the often-heroic struggles within local and ordinary lives as people aspired to a better way in and around the small-holdings of the country.

# 1

# Out Of The Darkness

From the double ditch, bared of its summer coat in a strange preparation for the winter's cold of November, he emerged, his arms fighting to push the brambles away, his face contorted with worry and his eyes furtively scanning over to where I was standing.

"The rustlers have taken them all," he shouted across, looking and sounding totally crestfallen. "There's not a beast left in any of the fields or the laneway."

For a moment his face twitched and I thought he was about to cry. Looking over the 50 yards from where I had been nailing a wooden stake post at the entrance gate, he appeared more like a scarecrow than a human being.

I hurried to where he stood, beside the wire rows of a fence between our neighbours and our land and put my arm around him to comfort him.

"We sold them, Da," I said gently. "We sold them. Don't you remember. We got rid of all the cattle bar the cows and a few calves last Monday in the sales."

"Did we?" he asked, his eyes checking my face to see if I was mocking him or telling the truth.

I felt a rising anger that he was forgetting such things. I was also scared that he was no longer the man who was emphatic about everything, particularly the judgment part of his own decision-making.

"It was your call," I stressed. "You said we didn't have enough fodder for them over the winter so we did what you directed."

He cowed in front of me, just like I had been a headmaster in school denigrating his work.

Immediately I was suffused with a deep sense of guilt as we both walked in silence towards the car. It was a cold early winter's evening and dusk was falling rapidly around us.

"God, it is a miserable night," I said, more to break the silence than to comment on what was already apparent.

"Let's get home and light a fire and have a bit of supper and we'll feel better before we milk the cows."

"I'd love a hot cup of tea," he said emotionally, as

if he was fighting back tears. "It will help get my ould head working right again."

•   •   •

Three days later I went to visit him in the hospital. Although I was only 17, I had been forced to take over the farm in the previous 72 hours. With my mother long since deceased and my brother in university in Dublin, I was the only one left to look after him at home.

The shock of listening to him struggle to find reality down the fields had frightened me more than the tales of ghosts or devils I had heard about when a child and ramblers came calling to tell their stories of supernatural existence.

I felt a sense of helplessness watching him stumble to stand upright in life; it was as if sand was shifting below his feet, forcing him to work hard just to keep his balance. I was conflicted between shouting at him to 'snap out of it' and wanting to act as a buffer for him against a world he was finding hard to face up to at that moment.

His scrambled state finally convinced me to call the doctor when we got home. He came almost immediately – I had just managed to light the fire, boil the kettle and was wondering if I would begin milking the cows myself when his car pulled up outside the house.

The doctor was a big, well-dressed gentle man

who was revered in our family. This stemmed from an occasion some 20 years earlier when my father was weak with double pneumonia and my mother's fear was that his laboured breathing wouldn't get him past the night.

In near-panic, she jumped out of bed and ran to knock on the doctor's door at one o'clock in the morning. On this particular night, the doctor had recently retired to bed, having enjoying the largesse of a dinner party.

With a pyjama-top under his coat and a trousers pulled on over sockless shoes, he met my mother at the surgery door and then accompanied her across the streets to our house, his battered old bag in hand.

He was shocked at how low my father was and took a gamble of a double injection – something my mother surmised he mightn't have done in the cold light of day.

The bold decision had an instant impact and according to my mother within an hour she could see an improvement in my father's demeanour and by morning his colour had returned.

Ever since that night, the doctor had a place of reverence in our household. I felt slightly inadequate as I ushered him into our kitchen, where my father was located in front of a fledgling fire which was smoking the kitchen without catching properly.

I mentioned in the hall, sotto voce, that I was prompted to call him because my father had believed all the cattle were stolen and I told him that my worry was he was 'losing it.'

Then I raised my voice to alert my father that the doctor had arrived. My father greeted him with great warmth by shaking his hand without rising from the chair. The doctor came around so that he was observing him full on.

"What ails you at all? The young lad tells me you're not yourself?"

I had a fear of being fully present as he began talking but was also conscious that I needed to know what he thought of the situation. So like a shadow I tried to retreat behind the two lead actors and be an almost invisible part of the scene.

It was then I heard the front door open and my brother emerged from the outside gloom. I wondered if my Guardian Angel had sent him as seldom before or since did I feel so inadequate in a situation. Pointing into the kitchen, I whispered to him about the doctor being inside and the fact that our father wasn't well.

Instantly, he took over by walking into the kitchen, saluting the doctor with a great familiarity – he had been best friends with one of his sons in national school and often played up in the doctor's house when he was younger.

The doctor too seemed relieved to be dealing with someone a bit more senior than me and after enquiring how his studies were going, he gently directed him out towards the back-kitchen area, his big paternal arm enveloping my brother's shoulders.

There they too talked in hushed tones for a few minutes while I stoked the fire and watched my father's face for reaction to what was going on around him. His eyes were downcast and his overall appearance deferential as if he was afraid to look another subject in the eye.

Just watching him there, I felt a pang of great sadness. I felt like hugging him in the hope that the pain he was feeling inside would somehow disappear.

"Now," the doctor said gently as he came back into the kitchen. "You are run down. Badly run down. And your whole system is low as a result. I know you could fight it here at home and come through alright but would you take my advice and go down to the hospital for a few weeks and you'll be right as rain before you know it?"

He looked up at the doctor and his eyes fixed on his face as he spoke.

He glanced across at me before staring into the fire for a moment and then looked up at the doctor again.

"Whatever you say doctor," he said in the meekest of voices. "Whatever you think is best, I'll do," he added in a whisper.

My brother took him to the hospital that evening while I did the chores at home and he also did the visit the next day before having to head back to catch up on his studies and lectures.

On the third day, I arranged to go down with my cousin to visit, having come to terms with a series of 'taboos' I never knew existed in our family.

Back then, every family had a skeleton in the cupboard – ours I told myself at that time was that we had a strain of madness pumping through our veins.

As I was collecting my cousin to accompany me on the journey to Portlaoise, my aunt could see that I was struggling to come to grips with all that was happening.

"Your father is one of the finest and most decent men who ever stood in shoe-leather in this town. If he broke a leg and was in hospital, you wouldn't feel embarrassed about it. He is, as the doctor said, a bit run down and his mind needs a bit of fixing. That's all it is."

I don't know if I totally agreed with her or not but her words were transformational as far as I was concerned.

I could now explain to myself what had happened and I was relieved that I could look on my father without feeling ashamed at where he had ended up.

In the end, it wasn't my cousin but my uncle – my father's brother – who came with me.

Normally, he was a great talker with a propensity to see the funny side of things; which left me a little perplexed after we had travelled for seven miles before he even tried to engage in conversation.

He opened up by asking me how I felt my father might have gone off beam and I told him the story about the cattle which he thought had been rustled.

"Ah, it was much the same the last time," he said.

"The last time," I interjected. "What last time?"

"Just after you were born."

I was just trying to get over what I had witnessed over the previous days when this revelation hit me like a hard punch in the solar plexus.

My uncle could see that I was trying to cope with something that had been withheld from me up to that point. As a distraction I began to open letters which had arrived earlier at our house but which I had not got round to reading.

The last thing I wanted to do was listen to my uncle lift another veil on a past I had no idea existed. I felt opening the envelopes might halt him in his tracks and stop him from talking further. Better still, I thought, if I close my eyes, I'll be able to pretend I didn't hear what he had just said.

"It's life," he said after what seemed an age, as he put his free hand on my shoulder. "We all need a bit of minding at some time or other and your father needs it now. Just like the last time. That came about after a tough year when the worry got in on him about all the sheep that were being killed by packs of dogs from the town. I went down to your house to see how he was. He was sitting in the chair beside the fire and the first thing he said to me was: 'We'll have to shoot the dogs.'"

"I went down the yard with the gun, aimed two shots into the dung-heap and came in and told him I'd killed them."

My uncle looked across sympathetically at me because my face must have shown the panic and confusion that I was feeling inside. My head was swimming with negative thoughts.

The thing I remember most was wondering what people – neighbours and friends – would think of me now that it was known my father was back in that place.

Then an even greater thought came into my mind – had we been the laughing stock of the town since the time I was born without my ever realising it?

I was wishing the ground would open up and swallow me by the time I heard my uncle's voice again.

"What your aunt said there earlier is true, you know. Your father is not some nutcase but a man who works too hard and is now a little out of sorts."

He then began to laugh. "When I went to visit him the first time there, I think the only problem he had on his mind was that I had shot the dogs. He loved them dogs but imagined in his head they, like the packs from the town, were killing sheep and that was why he'd told me to put them down.

"Do you know what I had to do?

"I left your Mammy with him in the hospital for over an hour as I drove back to the house, put the two dogs on leads and threw them into the back seat of the car.

"You should have seen his face when I walked the pair down to his bedside as everyone on the ward wondered if I was as mad as they were."

All the patients and the ward assistants gave us a round of applause as if we were at a dog show.

My uncle laughed so hard at the memory of the occasion that he half-took his own breath away and had to swerve to avoid the ditch as he drove.

After composing himself, he looked earnestly in my direction. "It was the best medicine anyone ever got in such a place. The dogs yelped with delight at seeing him and I don't know whether it was that or the head nurse running me and the dogs out of her hospital which gave your father the greatest lift. Anyway, as I remember, he was home in no-time, his batteries fully charged and ready to go again."

By this stage we had arrived in the grounds and were parking the car in front of the main entrance of the bleak and austere hospital building. A man from our town, who my uncle knew from childhood, but I had never seen before, came up to the car and shook his hand.

"I haven't seen you for years," said my uncle. "Don't tell me you're in here since.. since..."

"Since your brother was in the last time.." the man replied.

"Is it that long," my uncle asked incredulously?

Then, as an afterthought, he turned to me and pointed to the man. "Since this lad was a baby."

The man looked at me, held out his hand, and I shook it saying, "Pleased to meet you," as I had been always told to say to a stranger, even though I thought he was someone straight out of One Flew Over The Cuckoo's Nest and my skin crawled at the thought of my flesh pressing his.

My uncle put his hand into his pocket, drew out a few notes and gave the man a fiver. "Keep an eye on him for me," he said, pointing inside and obviously referring to my father.

"Oh, I will for sure," the man answered as he bowed in thanksgiving for the generous gift "He was a bit lost there when he came in but he is improving now," he shouted after us.

"Good," my uncle said with a wink back in the man's direction. "That's good to hear."

He continued to follow, telling us what ward my father was in, pointing the way to follow down the corridor and then left in a half-trot as if he had another mission to suddenly complete.

"The poor soul," said my uncle. 'You know he is as sane as you and me put together but he's stuck in here because no one wants him on the outside. The poor ould divil," he repeated.

•  •  •

"I'm sorry, goson, I'm really sorry that those lads stole the cattle," my father shouted down the ward to me when he saw me and my uncle enter.

I raised my arm in greeting as I hurried in his direction. He was still thinking about the cattle and the rustling. I told him everything had been sorted, which was the case, but he didn't believe me. "We'll all end up in the poorhouse now with the cattle gone," he said.

It was then I thanked my lucky stars that I had brought our post for the day with me. As my uncle drove down in our car, and between the revelations with which he had rocked my being, I had opened three or four letters; one was from the mart company with an accompanying cheque for four thousand pounds – payment for the cattle we had sold the previous week. It was a real stroke of luck that I had decided to bring them with me.

"Look," I said to him, as I took the cheque out of my inside pocket. "There's the proof that everything is ok."

I handed him his glasses from the bedside locker and he read the cheque out loud.... "Please pay... the sum of.... Signed..."

He took his glasses off and a sense of relief rushed across his face.

He then turned and smiled at my uncle and

greeted him warmly. He handed me back the cheque and told me to lodge it first thing the next morning.

"I will, of course," I agreed, "but will you also promise me to stop worrying your head over money.... Now that we are rich."

He laughed. "Rich. Sure that wouldn't buy more than a few calves to replace what we sold."

"Well at least it will be there and not gone off with some robbers," I chided gently.

He looked me in the eye, there was a sparkle back in the light blue colour that had disappeared for the previous weeks.

"Have you seen a doctor yet?" I asked, trying to both change from the thorny subject of money and also to find out if anything had been done for him.

"I don't know," he said sounding a little perplexed as he tried to work back in his mind what had happened around him for the previous days.

"Did they give you anything to take?" my uncle asked.

Again my father shook his head gently, more in affirming that he wasn't sure rather than he didn't know.

"Well, you'll want to be getting better soon," I urged, "as we won't feel till it's Christmas and we'll have the ewes yeaning. And then we'll have to start buying in stock in the spring to replace what we sold."

He nodded in agreement and I could sense that following the panic of thinking he had lost the cattle, almost immediately a serenity descended on him that I hadn't seen before.

"You know what!," I said to him, tapping into the moment. "I don't think there's too much wrong with you anymore."

He reached for his pipe on the locker beside him, lit the tobacco and inhaled deeply.

The blue smoke rose around his head up towards the ceiling, scenting the dorm from the strong smell of disinfectant which I noticed from the moment I had walked in.

We watched him as if he was an artist weaving patterns, blowing the smoke across our eyes and around the bed.

He drew on his pipe and for the first time in a long time, he pursued something with real zeal and zest.

I had never been in such a hospital before or even thought about how minds work or don't work, but I felt sure that the news we had been paid for our stock had reignited something inside my father better than any medication could ever hope to do.

I knew he wouldn't be allowed home that day or maybe not even that week, but I also felt sure that it would only be a matter of time before he could sign himself out, having returned to good health.

I looked at him and could see his own exhilaration at finding the elixir which was allowing him to fight back. There was a light shining and soon he would no longer be afraid of the dark.

# 2

# The Nocturnal Symphony

**N**ight in all its mystery becomes something of a wonderland of sound around the fields of a farm and a farmhouse.

The cloak of darkness changed the mood of its feel from daytime so that from one ditch to the next in a field and across the nooks and crannies of every individual farm, there was a sense of fear and bewilderment at the same time.

If the wind blew from one direction, it heralded one set of sounds on its unfurling; if from the other, a totally different set of tones and textures.

Of all the creatures out on the nocturnal prowl, none evokes memory of the past more for me than those of a fox barking to its mate. It's primal, and conjures up slightly threatening imagery in your mind about what's going on within the animals' world. The beauty of the night is that those noise bursts are accompanied by long breaths of total silence.

It was as if the world was listening to itself.

Unlike today. There is so much noise in the world now with television, internet, mobile phones that we find it difficult to hear the quiet. Time was when the crackling Radio Éireann news at ten o'clock at night was the only invasion of outside noise into a farm kitchen. Thereafter, once the radio was turned off either to save its battery or the electricity, the dominant sound in a house was the ticking of the clock or perhaps the singing of a kettle on the fire as it approached boiling point.

We lived on the edge of the town and there was a time when we knew the sound of every car that passed up and down outside our house. Rural life of that time had such sound intimacies that you could trace the where and when of your neighbours' every movement.

In my mother's birthplace, where my aunt and uncle and my cousins lived, there was a much wider constituency of nightly noise. If you stood at the doorway some nights, it was as if the hush transported individual sounds down to you; the farmer at the head of the road closing the door on his dairy having finished his delivery rounds, the drone of an engine working late in a farmyard from the other side of the hill and the view of a car light appearing like a torch searching for direction beyond the bog on the big road. Nearer to home, the lonesome lowing of a cow up in my aunt's haggard at the graveyard shed after her calf had been weaned off her could bring a shiver down your the spine.

Every night had a thousand stars as an umbrella on the world below in that Ireland of the twentieth century that was a much darker place than the present. My early years coincided with a time when the country was straddling itself between the old ways of tilly lamps and candles and 'the electric' as it was called, which was coming into houses all over the country from the fifties onwards.

That didn't result in every room of every house getting the electricity like today; back then people were fearful of the cost and the safety of having so much power all over the house. Because of that, there were thousands of houses with electricity in one or two rooms and maybe a cowshed or gable-end yard light but left the other part of their dwellings to remain in the darkness it had only ever known.

That left many, many frightening dark places to worry about if you were young. In that Ireland religion, fire and brimstone, the fear of death and the after-life, fairies and ghosts managed to co-exist as if homogeneous parts of the one body. Who wasn't convinced that there were invisible beings watching our every move – particularly at night-time.

Bringing me home at night, my uncle was my interpreter on the many meanings of night that presented itself to us between his house and ours – a mile in distance.

I always held on tight to his hand as we walked in the middle of the road up hill and down dale to the outskirts of the town. There were ghosts and ghouls about and if one tried to swipe me, I felt sure he would hold onto me with his strong grip.

Those thoughts and fears would consume my head as we started out on our walk, but he had an amazing sense of calm about him. He was interested only in what he could see and within a short time, he would have me sucked inside his world.

As he smoked his cigarette, he had the habit of looking up to the sky while he exhaled to see what was going on in the sky-world above, as he called it.

Without fail, every time we walked at night, he searched the sky for traces of constellations that I had never heard of before.

He was a farmer who shouldn't have been; his brain was creative and interested in learning – in today's opportunity of educational advancement, he would have loved the fellowship of professors. He had the gift of speaking in epigrams and he seemed to think with pictures inside his head that he could effortlessly translate to those who listened to him – a natural born lecturer or teacher.

Every journey between the houses started with

the same question – "Find me the North star and we can go anywhere from there."

Of all the stories he would tell of black holes, satellite groups, milky ways and stars travelling light years in our direction, the one that has remained with me was his telling of how the three wise men set out for Bethlehem using the sky to guide them.

"That's all they had in this world to find out where they were going. Man first found his way around the earth by following the stars. It mightn't have been the north star they followed, but they got there by some star."

Obviously we didn't need the stars to get us home but they were the lights that shone the way as we walked down the road.

He would stop every now and then too to pick up on the sounds, some mellow and semi-muted from the fields behind the ditches, some striking and sharp from the hillside further over.

"Listen to that, a vixen out on the prowl," he would say. He could tell what neighbour might be in trouble if she got into the henhouse. Then as we heard coarser barking, he would explain. "That place has a few dogs. There'll be no chicken supper for the foxes at that farm tonight."

Going to sleep after such a walk, it was easy to dream. Your senses had been exposed to nature's night-time theatre of sound and action.

My nightcap was to take it all in and allow such a wonderful nocturnal symphony to escort my thoughts into the world of sleep.

# 3

# The Long Acre

'The Long Acre' was the roadside grass that many farmers and people with little or no land but who had livestock, grazed as a sort of supplementary to their home feeding.

We were the supreme beneficiaries of the Long Acre largesse. We had to be. With our house peculiarly located on the edge of a town and without a blade of grass directly attached to it, every morning after milking, we put our cows out into a big open green area space that acted as a park for the town.

It meant our animals first port of call every morning or evening after milking was to bow their heads towards grass not belonging to us.

Nearby, we had one field a few hundred yards

from the house which my mother bought so that we could keep the cows and calves there every night. It was only a few hilly acres and often we rented another field a little further up in the winter to avoid churning up the grass in our own land.

It meant that for daytime grazing right around the year, we had to drive the herd of cows down from the yard to where we had most of our land over a mile from the house.

'Drive' evolved from actually being on a bike behind the cows with a dog, to allowing the herd out by itself onto the unfenced 'Green Field' that they could graze across as they began their journey.

This was another of the daily chores. After the morning milking, you could take maybe 30 minutes or so over breakfast but then you had to make sure the cows didn't interfere with the busy car traffic along the Moate Road.

The advantage of walking or cycling slowly behind the cows was time you got to yourself to salute neighbours along the way as they went about their daily life. Each had their own jobs to pursue around their houses whether it was sowing potatoes or cabbage in their gardens or clipping their hedges.

There was the lovely old woman who would come to her front gate to look up into your face as she spoke because her sight had nearly gone. The gift she passed onto me was how she linked the decades back to my grandfather and grandmother's time.

Her spirit was full of happiness and she also had an immense gratefulness, even as she approached blindness, for the good health she had been given well into her eighties.

Further down the road there was a precise and gentle little woman who was forever running with a bucket to attend chickens or pigs or to gather the apples that had fallen overnight from her orchard in autumn.

Up at the head of the Green Road was a man who wasn't so much like a neighbour as a comedian granting you – or whoever passed that day – an audience as you came by.

Like many of his time, he appeared to be either cleaning or lighting his pipe, which was always the most integral prop in his story-telling. As he spoke, he used his elbows to take his weight as he leaned on his front garden wall.

Of all the yarns he told, it was the true story about him which elevated him to the status of funnyman legend in my father's estimation.

It was a time when the Black and Tans were in Ireland and he found himself surrounded by a number of the local militia up in Aughamore close to dusk one night. There was a curfew at the time and in these auxiliary soldiers' eyes, he had broken it. They demanded to know why he was out flouting their law and order regulations.

"My ass has strayed from the back of the house

and I'm out trying to find him," he explained.

The leader of the unit took out a black pair of binoculars from a bulky leather case, the strap of which was slung across his left shoulder allowing it to sit on top of his right hip.

As he put them up to his eyes, he scanned the countryside by sweeping across and back several times. The he fixed his gaze on one point and handed them carefully to our neighbour, directing him by pointing his finger to look past the fields to a bog road about a mile away in the distance.

"That black donkey down there, is it yours?" he asked gruffly.

Peering through such powerful glasses for the first time in his life, our neighbour blinked for a second or two as he got used to the screen. Holding the binoculars in one hand, he then held out the winkers he had in his other hand and said to the leader: "Aye, that's him alright. Here, put these on him while I hold this."

The other men laughed loudly at the humour of the man and even the leader smirked at this 'Oirish' man and his deadpan face as he delivered his line.

"Go and get him yourself, but be quick about it," he ordered. Our neighbour said his good-byes, fully aware that he had won that duel thanks to the sharpness of his wit.

●　　●　　●

Getting out onto the main road from our house to his could take 15 minutes depending on how long you spoke to those people along the way.

That busier road required whoever was in charge to keep close to the heels of the cows – it was necessary to warn traffic to slow down as the cows went from one side of the road to the other in pursuit of where the tastier grass was.

It seemed that on this road there was a sentry to salute you and wish you well on your day's work – people who knew our circumstance and would look out for a young lad and on occasion, would come out and help on the road to steer the cows to the margins so that traffic could pass.

Traversing that particularly long, long acre could take an hour or an hour and a half before putting the cows into one of our fields. By the time they reached this place, they were often so full of the long acre grass that they would go for a drink of water and then lie down to rest for hours before beginning to graze our own grass late in the afternoon.

In an era where grass was a currency and the clever management of the resource was crucial to keep cows in a good milking condition, my father took advantage of the clear disadvantage it was of having to walk milking stock such long distances every day.

His view was that if I rushed the cows down and

home, they would be unable to get that grass and lose energy in the rushed trotting-rate that I often preferred – particularly if I had an evening football game.

The county council never had to worry about getting machinery out to cut that stretch of the long acre my father used as his own but for all that, it was fraught with danger and most definitely would not be allowed by the more safety conscious authorities of the present day.

Our greatest rivals in this now almost mythical land zone – the Long Acre – were the travellers who came to our neck of the woods in the early and sometimes late summer seasons.

They had a tradition for decades of decamping onto the quiet roads around our lands almost as a birthright.

The road between our fields was where this family group came to, transforming it into a village within a few hours of their arrival.

They would reside there almost as if they were settled, carrying out jobs from dawn till dusk for up to a few months before moving on to their next destination.

There was a cooper who made barrels and buckets which he sold on to the likes of us; others worked at repairing iron cart wheels for people of the vicinity while some were blacksmiths, able to look after the welfare of their horse's hooves. Their tents or old fashioned, horse-drawn caravans pitched along both sides of the road usually had fires lighting at the mouth of each temporary dwelling, even in summertime, because there was so much free timber to be found along our fences.

These people were the true kings of the road and the long acre. Every day you could see their piebald horses eating voraciously the fresh grass as far as their spancil would allow. The travellers never worried about horses straying as they tied the animal's leg in such a way – a spancil – that they could only shuffle along a roadway for 10 or 15 yards before running out of rope. Within their targeted time in a specific area, they would have cleaned both sides of the road of grass by grazing in such a manner.

The summer days were vibrant with this village of people going about their business and inter-facing when times and commerce demanded it with the locals doing their work.

Settled people would stop to chat and sometimes go into the tents for a cup of tea while waiting for work to be done by the travelling tradesmen. Once as my father and I waited for such work to be completed, a young lad my age asked if he could have a ride on my blue bike.

This had been handed down from my brother to me and was my prized possession.

As I was thinking up an excuse to refuse his

cheeky request, my father butted in, telling him to go ahead. "Have you ever ridden a bike before?" he asked.

The young lad – a bit like me seconds before – thought about telling a lie but then said: "No, but I'd like to be able to ride it like him."

As he said that, he pointed straight at me.

"Bring him out into the Five Roods field and hold the bike until he gets the knack," my father directed.

"What if he breaks it," I said back with more than a slight sulk in my tone.

"No fear of that, I had to pay through the nose for it and it's a sturdy little machine," he stressed.

The boy was very thin and the smell of burnt sticks off him was quite noticeable. But he was very grateful and deferential to me and as we walked the bike past the gateway of the Square Field into where my father had directed, I developed a little sympathy.

"How much did the bike cost, Mister?" he asked.

It was the first time anyone had addressed me in such a manner and it made me feel important.

"It was for my brother's tenth birthday," I explained, "but I don't know the price."

"I'd say it was dear," he said. "It looks smashing."

He was probably about a year younger than I was but was slightly taller with long, gangly legs. He found it easy to throw them over the bike and could sit in the saddle with both his feet easily touching the ground.

The land was hard underneath which made it easier for him to pick up momentum. I began the lesson by pushing him on the bike, explaining that once I let go, he would have to keep pedalling to maintain his balance.

He nodded excitedly as we began to move forward. I ran halfway down the field holding on firmly to the frame underneath the saddle. Then, when he had gathered sufficient speed, I released my grip and let him off on his own.

His balance was good as he began to pedal forward until the ditch became perilously close. "Use the brakes to stop," I shouted after him but I knew it was too late. He tried to jump off the moving bike but his momentum propelled him at speed into the ditch while my bike – like a riderless horse in a race – went headlong into the fencing, both landing awkwardly after hitting a tree.

As I arrived up to him, he was extricating himself from the briars and had cuts on both hands from holding them out in front of himself to buffer his fall. He also got a deep nick right across his forehead from the barbed wire fence and began bleeding profusely from the cut.

As I surveyed the scene, I could see that the front wheel of my bike had become buckled in the collision and would have made that my priority except for the way the blood was spouting out of the young traveller's temple.

Having heard the commotion in the distance, my father ran up the road and took a short-cut over the fence to be with us in a matter of seconds.

He used his handkerchief to apply pressure on the boy's wound with his left hand as he put his right arm around his shoulders to help prop him up as he walked him back to the tent.

I managed to catch up, despite the problems posed by my limping bicycle, just as the boy's father and mother came to meet my father in their 'village' area.

They looked concerned but my father assured them their boy would be all right. He asked them to boil a kettle and spent some time cleaning the cut which he declared was "very deep".

"By right, he could do with a few stitches," he said. "He can come in with us to the doctor's if you like," he added.

The young boy recoiled from him at the thought. His mother too crunched up her face and said he'd be fine, adding that it wasn't a problem to have a scar there. The man thanked my father for his expertise at cleaning the wound.

●　　●　　●

When we arrived down the following day, the 'village people' had moved on except for an old man and woman who were finishing their packing.

My father enquired about the younger family and the little boy and the old man was clearly agitated at his question. Initially I felt the man was blaming me and my father for what had happened – but as he spoke, it became very clear that this wasn't the case.

"They're off to England. That's why we're moving so early this year," he said with a sadness and irritability rolled into one.

My father talked for a little while to them and then they mounted their pony and cart where all their belongings were tied down and headed for the Galway road on their return to the west.

The Long Acre changed that year, not with us, as we drove the cows up and down for a good few years after that, but for the travellers.

They didn't come back the following or subsequent years. The call of a different and more modern life was heard by the younger set in this community too and many ended up relocating to England.

Somewhere over there I presume there is now a man with a distinct scar running down one temple from a fall off my little blue bike – which despite my fathers efforts to unbuckle the front wheel, never worked properly again.

# 4

# The Whip Hand

Rural Ireland had many traditions when it came to marriage; the main one saw a woman marry into a farm and bring something with her by way of a financial package, a number of cattle or a field or two of her own.

Love and marriage was something that could grow – once the business of a proposed union was hammered out in an agreement to both sides' satisfaction.

My aunt as a young woman was called in to arbitrate on one such marriage and on the morning of the proposed union there was so much disagreement that one side was prepared to walk away instead of walking down the aisle.

As the bride was being dressed for the occasion and the groom was cleaning himself up before putting on his brand new suit, frantic negotiations were being undertaken in a (friendly) neighbour's house in the hope of resolving the problem.

It was only when one side reverted to what they had originally promised to bring to the party that the green light was given for the occasion to proceed.

Less common arrangements in the generation before mine occurred when an only daughter in a farm and a man either with land or money or maybe sometimes a trade, wed into such a holding.

In the more conventional marriages, the man maintained his role as 'the boss' in the new marriage arrangement; however it often turned out that when it was the woman who owned the land, invariably she held the whip hand during the marriage in terms of finances and deciding the major issues in the business.

That worked out all right in some instances but in others it led to conflict or an on-going situation where the man – shamed slightly in his standing among his farming peers – would resort to deceit in order to keep his end up in the pub or while out enjoying social occasions.

We had one such neighbour during our time growing up and compounding his trickery on his wife was the fact that they had not been blessed with children over the 20 years of their union.

Without having the primary responsibility of financially running the farm, his daily raison d'etre grew into getting as much money as he could to buy drink in the pub.

By the time he chose me – without my knowledge it must be added – to be complicit in some of his schemes, he had become a past-master at delivering stories to 'herself' which were at time so credible through his delivery that I ended up half-believing them myself.

Although they lived just over a mile away from us, it was only when his wife bought a 20-acre field adjoining one of ours that my family got to know him. This was a field that had great water, a bit of a forest in one end which acted as shelter during the hot days of summer but more importantly during the long cold winters days when it was like a 'shed outside' for the cattle.

While his wife would ride down on her bike to herd the cattle periodically during the summer, once the land got wet and the evenings got dark early, she would leave that chore to her husband until well into the spring of the following year.

With such a time span to cover his ground, the man would invent different plans to sell off one or two of the cattle and worry about the consequences when they arrived at his door.

Unfortunately for himself, he would often give away too much information when he had a drink or two too much and then he would have to show remarkable mental agility – and in fairness he invariably did, by coming up with an excuse on the spot which more than satisfied his wife's enquiries.

For instance, having helped him in the autumn of the year to load a few bullocks into a truck which I assumed were for sale in a legitimate manner, I forgot all about the matter until he had me up in his house helping him with some chore many months later.

After dinner in the middle of the day on every farm at that time, he was enjoying his cup of tea and cigarette and talking optimistically about the good foresight they had shown in buying that parcel of land next to us.

'Look at that bit of ground," he said making his point. "Isn't it a great run of land that I haven't to bring down a tráneen of hay the whole winter and it is still able to support 18 cattle."

He paused to inhale his untipped cigarette.

"Twenty, you mean", she corrected immediately. "We've 20 head of cattle down there in Gurteen."

In the silence of the kitchen, you could almost hear the alarm bells go off inside his head.

Here was a situation where a man had clearly shot himself in the foot with his own tongue.

He also had to contend with the possibility that I, in my innocence, might jump in with the memory of the two cattle being loaded up the previous autumn.

Seeking to close off that avenue, he sought out my gaze and then with a clear wink out of her view that he needed my backing, he continued: "Sure this goson will tell ya that back in October I went down one day and two of our finest bullocks had their legs in the air as dead as door nails."

By now, he had jumped up from sitting at the table to command attention in the centre of the floor. Like an actor seeking to win over his audience, he put his arm up towards the ceiling before declaring: "I hadn't the heart to come home and break that sort of news to ya because I knew how upset you'd be."

Then officially addressing me, he went on: "Tell her, didn't you help me put them into the Burnhouse (a service which collected dead animals for free in our area) lorry? Both sets of eyes were now looking at me.

If I told the truth, I was damned by him and if I didn't, well I was damning myself by agreeing with this lie and fooling the decent woman which his wife was.

"Oh, for sure, I helped him load two bullocks alright Mrs," I said, a statement which was true when taken out of its real context – by not mentioning that the animals were alive.

How he was never found out could be due to the innocence of his wife or his own ability to tell a very plausible tale when his back was to the wall. From where I was standing that day, it was very much the latter which impressed me.

Sometime later I was drawing hay in for him with the tractor or 'the engine' as he called it and after a heavy morning's work, we sat down for a dinner of bacon and cabbage.

As she was dishing up the food, his wife apologised to me for how poor their homegrown potatoes were. "We've nothing only prateens this year," she explained, a description which meant the spuds were all the size of marbles.

"What are yours like?" she asked.

"Well," I said trying to stay on middle ground, "they're a bit better than those all right."

The man grunted in the background. I knew it was a code to me to leave it at that so I decided to keep my head down and concentrate on what was on the plate.

Instead of working with the hay in the afternoon, he diverted me to drive straight on instead of turning to the left when we reached the crossroads.

We drove to his potato field and he directed me to take the tractor down to one of the lower corners. There, under a tarpaulin, he unveiled a hidden pit in which he had eight jute bags full of the most splendid potatoes.

I helped him load the bags and when we got to the gate, he directed me to turn right and head for the town rather than the other way towards his home.

He had the afternoon all planned. Potatoes were

scarce that year because of the unusually fine summer and he was getting a premium price off one of the shopkeepers in the town.

We reversed in to the back of the shop to land the prize bags at the outhouse store.

"Leave the engine there," he ordered, "and we'll have a 'whet' before going back to work." I did as ordered and joined him in the lounge at the back of the multi-purpose premises.

He was in heaven in this moment as he ordered a half-one and a bottle of stout for himself and "an orange for the goson."

He threw the whiskey down the gullet in one sharp movement of the right arm, then began the pleasurable but time-consuming moments of pouring the stout into the half-pint glass.

He put the glass and bottle on the counter and as it was settling under a frothy head, he lifted his cap with his left hand and ran his right hand backwards on the fine dark mane.

"Drink up," he shouted over to me, pointing at the orange and enjoying his own joke.

Just then the shopkeeper, who had gone into a backroom to get an accounts book, returned behind the counter and began a course of adding and subtracting different sums from the value of the eight bags of potatoes.

She checked and then double-checked her figures under the guidance of her pencil, then turned to the till and took out about 75 pence and placed it in front of him.

His face tightened as if he had been shot in the back. He protested that her sums had to be wrong.

In the half-whisper which she employed to take him through the ledger, I could hear: "You bought a round the night of the Leinster final and that came to nine-fifty....."

And so on. And so on.

His premium rate for eight bags quickly reduced under the stacking up of such drinking nights against it.

He looked at the shopkeeper, at the 75 pence and pulled another face – this one had such disappointment written all over it that although I was trying to stifle laughter at the cameo I'd just witnessed, I ended up feeling a little sorry for him.

His trick had backfired. And if his wife only had prateens to eat for the rest of the year, he was virtually back to square one, except for the 75p which he threw into one of his trouser pockets.

He fingered the glass of stout, nodded to himself a few times as if working out a new plan, stood up and downed the Guinness in one mouthful.

"Drink up that orange," he said to me as if the very word 'orange' was anathema to his beliefs.

"We need to fill a few more bags for this woman or we won't have the price of a 'whet' for the weekend."

# 5

# 'The Gift'

She got the feeling of this 'gift', if you'd call it that, when she was a young woman at home one afternoon in the farmhouse. It was 'Black '47 and her brother, the one they all loved best, had been ailing in hospital with a sickness that wouldn't go away. They never spoke its name, it wasn't the done thing at the time.

Her mother wore a path either walking or cycling to the next town where the hospital was medically treating and caring for her sickly boy day after exasperating day.

My aunt in her twenties then, was young, dutiful and prayerful, in the hope that its power might restore health to her fourth oldest brother.

'The Gift' happened as she was kneeling in the kitchen saying her afternoon rosary – as she fed the beads between her right thumb and index finger, her concentration was broken by the sound of footsteps walking through the hall and up the creaking bare stairs.

She knew all the steps of the household – her mother's feather-light touch on the uneven timber, her eldest brother's strong pounding movement, the next brother's lighter but quicker touch between left and right foot. Only the memory of her long dead brother's foot, silenced then for over a quarter of a century, had she difficulty in recalling.

That thought slipped into her mind as she listened again to the noise from the staircase. These were her sick brother's steps – he was the one who always managed to find different notes of sound as he alighted the 12 steps to the top of the landing with his rhythmic foot movement of a tap dancer .

If she had any doubt, the sound of the backroom door opening with its complaining squeak and the rattle of the first floorboard to the foot of the entrant confirmed for her that her sick brother, the favourite sibling in the house, had come home at last.

As she scrambled off her knees and walked swiftly out into the hall in excitement to go up and greet him, her attention switched to the sound of a key being inserted into the front door.

A moment later her mother – dressed in black like all long-standing widows of that time – appeared in the hallway, squinting as she tried to adjust her sight from the brightness of outside to the darkness within.

"He's much better today," she said casually as she scanned the perplexed look on her youngest daughter's face which she mistook for concern about her brother.

My aunt was about to say she knew her brother was better because he was home and she was about to go up the stairs to his room to talk to him. Something inside intuitively quietened her as she sensed she was talking at cross purposes to her mother. Later she would explain that it was a moment of realisation in her life that brought her great sadness.

"I just knew then..." was all she would say by way of explanation.

That evening, after my father had finished work on the land and the milking much earlier than usual, word arrived back from the hospital through the Post Office mistress, that all the family should make the journey. When they got there, they were shocked to find that he was already dead and laid out in the morgue. His passing had come around the time my grandmother had returned to the house and my aunt had heard the steps.

She knew then that she had been given a forewarning but she kept the secret to herself for years. I don't know whether it was because I was her godson and was forever quizzing her on the history of our family that one day she told me this story but as she entered her seventies – some fifty years later – she found it easier to throw off the secrecy she obviously felt with that 'gift' as a young woman.

The next time it manifested itself was in the early sixties, sixteen years after the episode with her brother. By then she was married and living in a house up the road from where she was born and reared. Her mother, as was the custom, moved up to that house with her after my father and mother (and herself and her husband) married in a double wedding ceremony.

My granny enjoyed perfect health even as she pushed towards her eightieth birthday. Then in the early part of summer, she began to feel weak and unwell and was confined to bed. She had lived in a small middle-room but after a while my aunt moved her into the more spacious 'parlour' where she had erected a bigger and more comfortable bed.

In the afternoons when the dinner was over at half one and the house cleaned for the second time of the day, my aunt would sit in a wooden chair alongside the bed talking to my grandmother or more often than not just watching over her as she slept.

With her rosary beads in her hand, she whispered the Hail Marys to herself, praying for those close to her as well as those in need in Africa or wherever there was toil and suffering. That was the make-up of that generation, selfless and God-fearing in the best sense of the term.

Life had not been easy for my aunt, her first born – a lovely baby girl – had entered and departed this world in the same hour. It was a burden she carried with great understanding until finally many years later she gave birth to a son – my cousin who I grew up with like a brother.

That day as she prayed beside her mother, she saw a young girl in golden ringlets and white cotton dress enter through the open gate and head towards the door. My aunt moved swiftly to get to the front door before the knocking woke up my granny but was surprised to find no one there when she opened it. For a second she was curious as to where the child had got to until... it hit her like a brick between the eyes. The pathway in was straight but in her recall of the previous moments, she saw the little girl enter as if on an arc from the hill-side of the house. Walk. No, the girl hadn't walked, but glided.

She put both hands to her stomach to ease the pain she felt inside. When she returned to the room, her mother's pert chin was upright, her cheeks gently puffing in and out. It was the saddest moment of my aunt's life as she again surveyed a scene which she knew would change – the woman who had raised her and six other children single-handedly after her husband's death, was now ready to be reunited with him. He had died following a fall from a horse when my aunt was a babe in arms some 45 years previously.

It was the thought of reunification in the next life rather than the parting of mother and daughter in this one which sustained my aunt through that evening and into the long goodnight.

In the early hours my granny took another turn and within minutes had passed away. My aunt cried the tears of great sadness but she told me many years later how they also were tears of joy at the continuity she found in the death. To her, the child coming to the gate was not a neighbour's girl coming to sell Silver Circle lines as she had originally thought but her own daughter signalling that our grandmother would not be alone at death. Far from it, she would have my aunt's own flesh and blood – the daughter who only lasted minutes cradled in her arm – to take her on the journey across the great divide.

While neither sickness nor death is welcome when they cross any threshold, they have a way of forging togetherness among those who are suffering the consequences of a loved one either feeling unwell or being taken from the family.

Since I was eight, my mother was out of the house most of the time in hospital fighting the good fight to beat cancer at a time when the country feared to recognise it. My mother's sister only ever referred to it as 'the lad'. While my mother never gave up until virtually her last breath, my two aunts, her sister on one side and my father's sister on the other side, did their best to take her place with my brother and myself.

It was my father's sister who experienced these premonitions but up to then it had been only to people directly within her own family. On the day before my mother died, my aunt was in hospital recovering from an operation. She had felt nauseous in the afternoon following the procedure but that evening after eating toast with her tea, she felt much better and slept well that night. She awoke the following morning to the sound of a short, sharp knocking on her door.

She called out: "Turn the handle" several times, before rising out of the bed to cross to open it herself. As she did so, the sound ceased and once again there was no one outside trying to get in.

The pain that such moments created in her stomach returned and as she struggled with the physical hurt of the previous day's operation while struggling back to her bed, it was what she felt from the premonition that made her weep silently as she collapsed back into the sheets.

At first she thought the warning was for her husband or one of her three brothers still alive at the time, then her thoughts turned to her only sister, a heavy smoker who had not yet turned sixty.

As her mind moved from the image of one face to

the next, the door opened and her brother-in-law entered with a look on his face which confirmed for her what she already knew – that there had been a death. He told her that my mother had passed away at ten minutes to midnight on the previous night.

I think the fact that she had received a warning about my mother's death made her more determined to do all in her power to mother my brother and I from then on. She cooked and washed for us but more importantly, she dispensed correction and wisdom in equal measure to us as we grew into teenagers and later adulthood.

She looked after my father when he took the selfless decision to send us both away to school so that we wouldn't 'have a life of drudgery trying to make a shilling on a farm of bog'.

Every day my aunt insisted that he would come to her house and eat with her, her husband and her son so that in our absence, he still was part of a family. From the time he was 14 and she was a baby, he had forged a special bond with her, standing in for the father she never knew alongside his widowed mother.

In turn, she felt there was no one like him, claiming that he minded her from the rough and tumble of the other siblings as she grew up the youngest of seven children. Now she was repaying that minding in daily kindnesses to him.

My father was an immensely strong man and

because her husband had recently suffered severe heart problems, he was only too happy to help out with any work my aunt and uncle had with their cattle or tillage. She knew that her husband could keel over at any minute if he undertook any hard work; the fact that my father would accompany him on such chores meant he was never put in that position and she didn't have to worry over her man collapsing and dying.

•  •  •

It was many years later when I was probably in my mid-twenties and my aunt was in her sixties that I did something that shocked her so much she would have had every right never to talk to me again.

The two of us sat in the kitchen of her house one fine evening drinking tea and enjoying our chat as we talked about the various family members to see where they fitted into our family tree.

As someone who was fascinated by her premonition stories, I raised the subject out of curiosity to see what she might say. Now that her husband was approaching seventy and her surviving brothers and sister had also nudged forward in the cycle of life, she said she wished those warnings would never come again.

Yet for some inexplicable reason, maybe it was that I was young and caught up in a moment of devilment, I told her I was going home. Instead, when I went outside, l lingered near her house for about 10 minutes, then returned and pressed on the bell at her front door. She came out almost straight away but by the time she had the door opened, I was hiding behind the pier. She went back in. A few minutes later I rang the bell again, this time 'lying' on it for emphasis before again withdrawing out of sight. She came out again, this time circling the house two or three times before re-entering.

I allowed a few minutes to elapse before I returned to the house and let myself in by the back door. By then, my aunt was sitting by the fire, cradled over, her face the colour of death. It was on seeing her there that I realised what an awful thing I had just done. Immediately, I felt an overwhelming sense of remorse and knew that I would have to blurt out the truth to save her further suffering.

"Are you ok?" I asked sheepishly.

"Yes," she said, clearly lying as she was fighting to remain calm.

"You didn't have any premonitions lately?" I ventured, slightly cheekily.

She looked into my eyes, more than a little perplexed at my question.

"How did you know?" she queried.

"I'm so sorry," I said. "That was me ringing the bells there. I thought it was a bit of fun. I didn't think it would frighten you so much."

She had every right to give me a clout and throw me out. Instead, she exhaled a huge sigh of relief and simply said as she made a large sign of the cross: "Thank God for that."

For about a month afterwards, I asked her to forgive me every time I called to see her. Then one day she told me to stop apologising as she felt there was a reason behind why I had done it. "I think that what you did was a sign that there won't be any more premonitions," she explained, though I wasn't sure how she arrived at such a conclusion.

She also said she knew that even though her husband was a decade older and had the complications of a bad heart, he would outlive her. "That was the premonition I dreaded but I now know it will never happen," she exclaimed with a palpable tone of comfort in her words. I knew from the assuredness with which she addressed me that she believed there could be no other outcome.

The woman had a saintly way of turning bad news into good and right through her life, that was her real gift. The other 'gift' was something I still don't understand, other than I'm sure she would have preferred not to have been given it.

As time went by, age and forgetfulness exasperated her life and as she reached the same stage in life as her mother, it was clear that she was confused between what used to happen and coping on a day to day basis. That spring, shortly before she died, I drove down from where I lived to see her one evening.

I had been living in Dublin for years but visited my home town to see her and my other aunt on a regular basis. I had no sooner arrived in the door than she ushered me into the living-room, where no one ventured into, except at Christmas time.

She took out an old biscuit tin and opened it. Inside, she had several groups of photos with elastic bands around them. She sifted through them, one by one, explaining who each person was. She was remarkably lucid during this exercise, as she was when explaining verbally why her sister had gone to live in Dublin and how a second marriage by her grandfather was as far back as she could go into our family history.

As she finished, I was about to ask her why she had done this when she put that long index finger of her right hand up in the air – as if to brook no argument – and began.

"I'm starting to forget things. I know it is important you know who's who in our family. And that book of short-stories you love over there on the dresser, I want you to have it after... well, when I go."

I was about to remonstrate with her on that issue by saying she looked well and would be with us for a long time to come but once again she raised that all-conquering finger.

"Stop. I know what I'm talking about," she said firmly.

Within a short period, she had become ill, had gone to hospital and died. At her funeral, we all grieved to our core for this special person who had blessed our lives. Sometime in the afternoon after she was interred in the soil close to her baby daughter and mother, the thought came to me that I should be happy; that what had happened was more a reunification for her than a parting – like she believed when her mother died.

The memory of the night when she summoned me into the living-room is something I have considered a thousand times down the decades. The only conclusion I can come to is that she had had a premonition of her own death and was fulfilling some earthly housework with me before allowing it to take place.

# 6

# The Man
# Who Was
# Happy

In any valley or townland in this country, you only needed to scratch the surface to find a microcosm of how the whole world lives and dies.

For every ambitious landowner trying to upsize even more, there were several small farmers working night and day to also increase either their holding or stock numbers and a variety of non-farming families with jobs in factories, offices or more specialised employment trying to pay their bills on any given week.

In such outposts as ours, you found human beings

constantly chasing rainbows, pursuing dreams and hoping to follow a road to serendipity paved with financial and personal riches.

Of course, what we seek is life's great conundrum but it hasn't stopped man treading that circuit from time immemorial.

Each generation believes they are the first to contest the challenge of living through the fury thrown at us and few, if any, ever come out the other side acknowledging that what they have undertaken was for the most part an exercise in futility.

It is easy to understand why though. As WB Yeats once said; "the richest man among us is the best." Whatever religion or whatever God looked down on us, he seldom could compete with the wondrous temptation of "adding halfpence to the pence."

Growing up, my world was about two and a half miles in diameter. In that circle the denizens fought for their share of whatever market they were involved in – each in his or her own inimitable style.

For instance, a distant neighbour of my uncle's one morning found a new calf up in the stony-field and shouted across the ditch between fields to him that the new arrival was the 100th member of the cattle community that he now owned.

A man of possession to be sure and a rich man among the Ireland of that day.

My uncle congratulated him on reaching such a

landmark in his life but was a little taken aback when he got no response from the man.

Wondering if his neighbour was ok, he slowly picked his way through the fresh undergrowth to peer into his neighbour's property.

By the time he got up to where he could see out through the thicket in the boundary fence, the man had gone away a distance of perhaps 150 yards down the field – urinating while he walked such was his hurry to get to his next chore.

Telling the story to my aunt and the rest of us in the house at supper time that evening, he sucked his Woodbine cigarette and declared: "If the only way a man can celebrate having 100 head of cattle is to piss while walking, I'd rather have half that and smell the roses that he didn't get around to wetting."

Another distant neighbour was struck with the same 'hurry stick'. He would not stop to talk regardless of the time of day or day of the week. His son told me the tale of being with his father in the car one day when the driver in the vehicle ahead failed to negotiate a dangerous bend and crashed through the fence and down into a hollow field.

Without even flicking an eye-lid, the local man drove on. When his child who was just out of primary school asked: "Would you not stop in case the driver needs help," he was told in no uncertain terms that there was work to be done, adding that he had no time to be following clowns through ditches.

While that was indeed an extreme case, there seemed to be little let up in work as people rose, worked and slept through a constant rhythm. In our farm and in those around and about us, people constantly pushed themselves in the chase for a better quality of life.

At that time in the sixties, some families were signing up contracts to provide beet to the sugar factories, others were embarking on crop rotations with winter wheat and barley while the greatest explosion at that time saw farmers virtually everywhere join up to become creamery milk suppliers.

At the same time, there was a more lucrative milk selling operation where farmers provided an agreed volume of milk on a 12-month basis to regional daily suppliers. Whereas the creamery milk farmers could send as many churns as they wished in the summer time, they didn't have to worry about the expense of winter feeding to keep milk yields up, unlike those who opted for the morning milk market into Irish homes. That was the first economic lesson of my life – sometimes you have to pay more to supply a product but because you do so, you get a greater return per gallon of milk than those riding the seasonal vagaries.

That was the seminal decade when farmers, even the creamery milk men, got a monthly cheque (for about eight months of the year) which allowed them to join a more modern agriculture economy than the previous level of hand-to-mouth subsistence.

In that world, farms would have to manage money carefully between events such as the selling of cattle at a fair and the sheep's wool that brought in a few much-needed pounds to the coffers during the often financially parched summer time.

My aunt's farm was more up to date than ours – they entered the great milk race the month before us and had the number 143 written in white paint on their single churn. When we started we got the numbers 145 – and had only one 10-gallon churn for the milkman to collect for all of that first year as a supplier.

My aunt and uncle also turned over their 'pump field,' as it was called, to a crop of sugar-beet which they sold to the factory in Tuam.

We were happy to have the milk-cheque coming in as a backbone to his earnings – a novel and welcome addition to how my father had provided for the house in the previous two score and ten years of his life.

He also had an economic rule of thumb that probably would have made him a mint on Wall St or among the massive farms of north America; his idea was to get into whatever everyone else was getting out of.

With the exception of joining the creamery, his quirky farm economics worked a treat for him.

I remember at one stage during the sixties and early seventies – and because of the wholesale selling of milk to creameries, most farmers couldn't wait to sell their calves to the cattle jobber.

This man was a great character but wasn't happy that this trend had emerged to spoil his business. Up to then, he used to drive down to the Golden Vale and other big milking areas of north Cork and Tipperary to buy calves at rock bottom prices. Indeed he often told the tale of buying 10 calves in one place and the farmer was only too happy to throw in another two just to get them out of the way of drinking his milk.

Never one to stop gilding the lily with a good story, he would later enlarge on this tale by saying that he once stopped at a pub on his way home to discover the population in the back of his lorry had doubled during his imbibing of a few shorts.

Back in the midlands he was able to talk up the pedigree of these calves while trying to strike a top dollar rate for the bulls and a slightly lesser price for the heifers.

That strategy was in grave peril as his local customers were now suppliers themselves and could see a quick buck in the milk-cheque unlike the rearing of calves on a bucket that didn't give financial returns for a few years.

The jobber wasn't a farmer himself and hated having to keep the calves in a shed behind his house when, as was happening more and more, he couldn't flog them off the evening he returned from the south.

Having had to hang on to one lot for a week, he made a valiant attempt to offload them a second time by doing the rounds of farms within close geographical reach.

Not only could he not get anyone to bid, there were several places he arrived at where the owners didn't even look into the back of his little truck to see what the stock was like.

In desperation, he turned to my father who could have held his own in a Las Vegas poker game when it came to feigning disinterest in something he wanted.

He paid him the good manners of looking in through the little window on the side of the lorry to see the calves.

"You'd want to feed them soon or you'll have the problem of burying them," he said rather unsympathetically to the beleaguered jobber.

Talk about the poor fella being over a barrel. In the end he was happy to give the calves away for virtually nothing – "it's the first time a luck-penny was the only payment I got for a sale," he later told my mother in the kitchen as he drank a half of whiskey to seal the deal.

My father's logic was simple. He had a scrub-bull in one of the backfields which ensured a number of heifers proved in calf every year. Many of these would not be the milking breeds of friesians or shorthorns but more likely would be whiteheads (Herefords) that were better for beef rearing than milk.

All he would do was get every new heifer with a calf to adopt one he had bought in – and so his logic went – they could be reared for free.

Sheep could be an economic curse or cure on a farm at any given period. With the expansion of family farms into the new forms of comparative riches with tillage and milk, many decided that sheep were more trouble than they were worth. The lambing season could be hit and miss and because a lot of the farms around our vicinity were close to the town, attacks from packs of dogs were more often a reality than a threat.

Around that time, he also bought more hoggets to breed. He was content that with the extra price for both lamb meat and wool because of the relative scarcity in our area, he would end up making money out of something that others were rejecting.

And so ran the interfacing world of commerce, social outlet and family rearing in our areas of uplands and moorlands – the good, the bad and the boggy which made up our fields at the time.

● ● ●

People urinating as they walked just like the animal kingdom, delivery men in vans getting seed and fertilisers to outlying farms and hardly having the time of day to salute anyone along the way is the over-riding memory of how that world revolved.

Only one person I knew – or more precisely observed – seemed beyond or at least detached from this daily freneticism.

He was an old IRA-man who had somehow landed in our part of the country some 50 to 60 miles away from his native Longford.

He lived in a galvanised shed in a little bit of no-man's-land across from where my mother was born and reared and which my aunt and uncle farmed.

The shed was corrugated iron on three sides with the wall side backing out onto the road. From there you could sometimes listen in to his world.

He invariably was humming as he built up his fire in the middle of his one room, you could hear the scalding reaction when he took his pipe out of his mouth to spit into the fire.

In summer he often sat out in front of his tigeen on a broken wall smoking his pipe and using his cap to fan himself when he felt too warm.

On the day of the month he got his old IRA pension, he would depart early to the town, buy his supplies and retire to a local hostelry. Later that evening, his long languid walk would become slightly exaggerated as his upper body shook each time an unsteady foot would explore the ground beneath him.

My cousin and I often hid behind the wall if we saw him coming in that state. Not that there was anything to witness – only a man with one hand continuously on his pipe puffing and humming at the same time.

I remember his lifestyle DNA impressing on ours on two major occasions. Once in high summer when we were all up on the tractor and trailer heading to pike hay for the day. My aunt saluted him as he sat in the shade of an elder tree surveying all around him.

'Hasn't that man got the life of Reilly?" she said to my uncle, more in approval than in any attempt to belittle the sort he was.

One August-time as we headed for the graveyard in Horseleap as part of the annual cemetery prayers for the dead, my aunt again saluted him with a big wave.

He stood up from his favourite outdoor position on the half-broken wall, took off his cap and gave a little bow in her direction.

"A great life for sure," my uncle said, as if replying to my aunt's previous statement of sometime before. "And he does it without fear or favour to God or man."

He was tall and thin and how he cooked and fed himself and kept body and soul together I don't know. He didn't routinely push himself on any house for food and was very independent in how he lived.

The winters in the midlands are colder than

anywhere else in Ireland and I often wondered as I lay in bed at night how he kept warm in a shed which could shelter him from the heat but not from the cold.

I remember being happy when another kindly neighbour did up an outhouse – more house than shed – and allowed him to transfer his wordly belongings in a small jute sack to that site about a hundred yards away from where he had previously resided.

Now he had a proper window in this little domain and a fire to keep him warm and a caring neighbour who did actually give him regular meals.

Life went on in our area – the man who urinated while walking continued to chase the rainbows which made him happy until he passed on, the man who didn't stop when the car crashed also died and all the men and women in the farms continued to work hard so that their offspring might get a little more out of life than what they themselves had growing up.

Only this quiet individual stayed the same. A man who arrived in our area one day, found a shed to stay in and seemed to have all the riches of happiness to hum his way through life.

I was away in school when he died peacefully in his sleep. The good neighbour who had given him the new dwelling hadn't seen him and when he knocked and got no answer, he opened the door to see him dead on a chair with the pipe on the floor beside him.

With neither kith nor kin in our area, my uncle and the kindly neighbour made contact through our own parish priest to see if he could arrange for the man to be buried in his native place. The parish priest in that area of Longford was contacted and agreed that there was a place in the pauper's plot for him.

It was my aunt who made the decision that her husband, my uncle, would hire a car, bring the neighbour with him and they would accompany this stranger among them on his final journey back to his own place.

At the graveside the priest said the prayers and two people – my uncle and his neighbour – stood on either side of the coffin responding to his bidding.

It was, my uncle later remarked to my aunt, both the saddest and most fulfilling funeral he had ever attended.

# 7
# Playing Games

My father had no time for the GAA. Like many people of his era he saw participation in sport largely as a waste of energy.

"I'll start following them when they put bread on the table," he'd say when we asked him why he never came to any of our matches.

He was of an age where pragmatism ruled – if you were out running after a ball for an hour during the week or at the weekend, you were wasting energy that could be put to better use, milking cows, cutting hedges or making hay. There was no room for compromise in this equation – balance between work and play could be best demonstrated by his mindset in the following example.

As our house was over a mile away from most of our land, we would often pack up food and stay down the fields for the day once we had done the morning chores in the yard.

Around two or three o'clock in the day, one of us would light a fire, boil the kettle and makes tea for the others working in the fields. We would then cut up the bread, make sandwiches etc and have what would appear to the outsider to be a 'picnic' in the middle of a working day.Except it was anything but.

My father appreciated that the body needed to be refuelled and would enjoy the tea-break before lighting up his pipe for a smoke.

Often as he did so, he would turn to me or my brother and say: "You should run down now and herd the cattle in Bentleys and Gurteen while you're resting yourself."

Bentley's was half a mile away down a long lane and rugged terrain. You then had to jump across a river, run another half mile before reaching our field in Gurteen. At the bottom of the second field, another half mile away was the well where you were expected to raise water for 30 head of cattle, before you ran back along the road, another mile to where we were working.

That was the guts of a three mile run and maybe raising 90 buckets of water from a well 10 feet under ground... all while you were, in my father's words, "resting yourself".

When you got back an hour and a half later, you were invariably greeted with the words "What kept ya?" as if you had been loitering with the intent of avoiding the 'real' work that was going on in the field he was in.

I'd hate to paint a picture here that my father was a tyrant. He was nothing of the sort. There were times he would be in bad humour but mostly he loved to chat and he had his own sense of mischief too. In fact, the more I think back on it, he was probably having a right laugh at my brother and I when he would issues such orders ..."while you are resting yourself".

As a family we weren't the earliest risers but maybe that was because my father never knew when to quit at the other end of the day.

When I visited my friend's farm in Wexford as a teenager, I wasn't surprised to see that they began milking at seven o'clock in the morning; the real eye-opener was that no matter what job they were doing out in the fields, the father in that household downed tools at four in the afternoon and had the milking and other farmyard chores completed by six o'clock.

Back home, we would only be warming up for 'a good evening's work' in my father's mind after we had a second tea-break in the field around that time.

Maybe an hour into that late shift, he would turn to me and say: "You round up the cows and get them home and we'll stay on here for another while and then catch up with you."

Myself and the dogs, Darkie and Shep would dutifully go to the fields where the cows were and begin the long walk of over a mile to the farmyard while my brother and father worked on until they decided they had enough and headed home to milk whatever cows I still hadn't got around to.

Depending on how much work they stayed to do, I might have six of the 12 cows milked before they would arrive. After that, while they finished off that job, I would be deputed to strain the milk and deliver it to those neighbours who were customers of ours.

Then sometime before dark, and with no woman in the house, we would start cooking some sort of evening meal. Hardly a day went by but we'd find that we had no butter or tea or bread; so a quick expedition to the shop was required before we could throw up a meal on the table.

This was at a time when there was only one channel on most televisions outside of the main population centres on the east coast, so to relax, we were totally dependent on whatever the chiefs in RTE decided was entertainment post 10pm – Cannon, Mannix or Colombo. All mindless stuff but after a day of travelling miles either counting or watering cattle and walking cows to and from the land (not to mention the main day's work), I could have looked at such inane TV all night.

It was ok if my father got involved in the story of the plot – and he particularly loved Cannon – but sometimes, like the year of the World Cup in Mexico in 1970, matches went on into the wee hours and there were some incredible games at that. England and Brazil of a Sunday evening, Italy and Germany and then of course Brazil and Italy in the final.

Inevitably somewhere in the middle of one of those games, he would initiate proceedings for the rosary. As we got older, we resisted this more and more but inevitably gave in as he was after all, the boss of the house. However, we managed to negotiate certain conditions – that we would say the rosary during half-time in one of those matches and we would reduce the 'trimmings' (all the prayers for special intentions after the five decades were recanted) through agreement.

In my sixteenth year, I had developed a great love for Gaelic football and was made captain of the club's juvenile team. Several of the earlier rounds of games were played on midweek days during those long summer evenings, with 7.30 and 8.0 throw-ins very common.

That was fine for 99 per cent of the population whose fathers were happy to end their working day at six o'clock but as we've seen, the day in our household was only swinging into full gear at that stage.

He would have laughed me out of court if I had

suggested that we all end the day early so that I could play "with that GAA crowd". Under such circumstances, I had no choice but to introduce a sense of subterfuge to plan an early escape.

Obviously that could not be done alone – it was vital that my brother bought into the deceit, otherwise there was no chance of moving my father from the land at an hour which gave me a chance to be in time for the minibus which took us to our games.

The big game for us that year was fixed for midweek and my first hope for the day was that it would be raining sufficiently so that we would not be down in the fields. For some reason, every time I prayed for a favour, I got the opposite result.

I knew from early morning just by looking at the sky that it would be a corker of a day. And so it turned out. As my brother and myself were turning the hay with forks in the Square Field, we hatched a plan to ensure I got home by seven o'clock.

It involved getting to my father's waistcoat where he kept his big, old-fashioned pocket-watch and putting the time forward by 90 minutes. Often, on a hot day, he would still keep his waistcoat on but that day the first bit of luck fell our way when the heat of the sun forced him to hang his vestment up on a knob of an overhanging branch of a sally tree.

When my father decided he would go around the ditches and collect wood to light the fire, I used his absence to put his watch forward the requisite time.

We worked on as usual but the only worry was that the six o'clock angelus bell from the town would waft all the way on the breeze down to where we were.

There were times when you could hear the bell clearly and then on occasions you would only barely detect it if you listened. We kept our guard up and on the day as the first chime was picked up by my brother, he burst into a loud rendition of the Rolling Stones song 'Time is on our side,' winking at me as to what he was doing.

I joined in, maybe a little too vigorously as we drowned whatever little toll that came across the fields. It led to my father stopping work, looking at the two of us with a sense of bewilderment and exclaiming with a real sense of incredulity: "Are ye two fellas right in the heads?"

About ten minutes later, we began muttering that it must be time to get the cows. My father laughed at us, saying it was probably only after four.

We persisted and in an attempt to make him play ball my brother suggested, as casually as was possible under the circumstances, that maybe he should check his watch.

Possibly with the intention of shutting us up, he immediately stuck his two-grain fork in the ground like a spear and walked over to the tree where his waistcoat was hanging and rummaged through his pocket for the time-piece. I had to suppress a fit of the giggles as in the distance I first saw him look at the watch, then put it up to his right ear to check it was working and then shake it several times.

"I don't believe it. Only it's my own watch, I'd say it was wrong. Where has the day gone?" he asked no one in particular.

We waited a few minutes to see would he go with his gut and keep us working or accept that his watch, which he often claimed hadn't lost a minute in 10 years, was telling the truth.

"You better round up the cows so," he shouted over to me.

No sooner had the words been uttered than I dropped the fork, called the dog and sprinted across to the Sally Gardens where the cows were located for the summer days.

Although the cows normally liked to graze slowly along the long acre as they walked home, that night I had an ash plant which I threatened them with as we headed out onto the main road.

One of our cows had a straight hind leg from an accident but even she had to smarten her pace on the night as I whipped up something of a stampede to meet my deadline.

I'd agreed with my brother that I would milk three cows and he would take up whatever slack I had left behind. I also left it to him to come up with whatever excuse he could think of to explain my disappearance, not to mention how, when my father saw the kitchen clock, he would realise he was home and finished work so much earlier than normal.

That I knew would take some explaining, but no better man than my brother to perform under pressure. The smell of sweat, cow dung and milk is a potent aroma which would knock warts off a mule. Having rushed the cows home, I was perspiring liberally on such a fine evening and there is no better (or worse) job to open the pores than milking by hand at such a time.

I knew I'd have to wash before jumping into a mini-bus with 20 or so other lads or they would all pass out with the rotten aroma. We had a barrel full of rain water forever at our back gable and I immersed myself fully in that with a shorts on – all the while washing hair and my hands with carbolic soap.

It mightn't get the same results as Head & Shoulders but it did the trick. A quick towelling to dry, then jump into my good clothes and I was waiting for the minibus horn to sound.

As I searched for my boots – plastic ones which were the cheapest on the market – I was shocked to find them under the stairs in pieces. I don't know how this happened other than one of the dogs must have begun playing with them and didn't stop till they were ripped asunder.

In truth, it took little effort to pull them apart. They had already two big cuts across the middle cogs which I previously had tied up with a black tape my father had for mending leaks in water pipes around the yard.

The tooting on the horn meant I had no time to see if I could borrow a pair from anybody close by.

I headed out to meet the rest of the team with a plastic bag with a pair of togs and football socks.

"Where's your boots," the mentor asked, seeing how slack my 'kit' appeared in the bag.

"Eh, I can't find them," I said lying.

"Has anyone another pair of boots with them, lads?" he shouted back into the bus from the front where he was perched.

No one had.

"C'mon anyway, sure you can play in your bare feet like Babs Keating," he laughed, much to my embarrassment and to the merriment of the rest of his crew.

We stopped at a few houses along the way but no one had my size available. I was mortified at the feeling the other lads must have that we couldn't afford a pair of boots. But as I said previously, GAA or its apparel or indeed footwear was not a priority on my father's spending list.

In the end, I had no option but to tog out with my 'Sunday' slip-on shoes as footwear. My marker shook my hand before the throw-in, looked down and said exactly what he shouldn't.

"No boots out yere way?" he sniggered.

I felt jaded before I togged out for the game. Between the dashing from the fields home and then the disappointment of having no boots, my energy was totally sapped.

I played midfield and his remark was what I needed. Every time I caught or went for a ball, I had only one thing on my mind – to beat my marker (and his pair of Blackthorns I would have died to have owned).

I'm not sure how well I played; one of my teammates said I might try high-heels the next time which drew a big laugh. All I know is we won easily enough and went on to reach the final.

We had a sing-song on the way home in the little bus with one or two of the lads singing 'dirty songs' which I heard for the first time. The grown-ups in the front – the driver and the mentor, pretended to be cross at these versions but I could see them laughing away at the fun in the words.

It was dark by the time we arrived back into the town. I hurried home and slipped in the back door to the kitchen. My brother had gone out to the pictures with one of our cousins and my father was by himself looking at the black and white flickering television which you felt sure was about to blow up at any minute.

I lingered for a few moments inside the door wondering what he might say.

"Did ye win it?" he asked in an upbeat tone – something that totally surprised me.

"Aye," I said in astonishment, calculating that trying to lie about where I had been would be a waste of time.

"We did."

I clumsily tried to keep a cool exterior as I plugged in the electric kettle to make myself a cup of tea.

"Do you want a cup?" I asked looking over at him for the first time.

"I wouldn't say no to one," he said chirpily.

After wetting the loose tea and cutting two slices of brown bread and butter for him and myself – our nightcap meal – I handed him the cup and plate in the soft chair by the fireplace

"How did you find out about our match anyway?" I enquired, sounding as casual as I could.

He took a sip of the tea, deliberated as he stirred the sugar around with the teaspoon and then looked beyond me and as if addressing the dwarfed Cannon, on our malfunctioning television at the other side of the room.

"I met one of your GAA head buck-cats at the Novena the other night and he asked me to make sure you were ready in time for the game.

"That being the case", he went on, "wasn't it a good job we finished the hay early this evening."

# 8

# The Unholy Trinity

**W**hen Ireland was in the grips of the Catholic Church, it was a most unforgiving, at times almost unchristian place to live. People sat through endless hours of their lives listening to the priests' roll call from the pulpit how much 'dues' every house in the parish contributed to their welfare.

On most Sundays, there were long sermons to help save our souls during the upcoming week. But when the Christmas, Easter or Harvest 'dues' were in, those long and boring homilies were put aside for the Church's version of a town's soap opera.

So who gave what to the big parish pot? Well, the doctor, the businessmen and the big farmers gave

10 shillings, the bank manager seven and six, the shop owners five shillings, the small farmers and businessmen half-a-crown, the workers two bob and the widows and the unemployed a shilling.

Every name, every house identified from the pulpit and at home later over every dinner in the parish on such a Sunday, those who didn't contribute would be identified from the fact that their names were not read out.

Once, we failed to get the half-a-crown in on time; leaving mass that day the stares of the flock were on us. That led to a great row in the house as to who was responsible for not getting our dues in on time. Fortunately, there was a sort of repechage on the following Sunday, where a small section of the homily time was given over to calling out the names of those who had failed to give the money on time.

The Church was the central edifice in most towns and villages and the 'men of the cloth' were the most powerful.

Woe betide anyone who disagreed with a priest or for one reason or another threw cross words in their direction. If a person fell a bike six months later, that mishap would be traced back to such an incident with a clear understanding that he only got his due for having the temerity to take on one of God's anointed.

By far the saddest part of all day-to-day living in rural and small town communities was the damning judgement handed down by those daily and Sunday altar-rail visitors when it came to the misfortunes of their neighbours.

It was a strange kind of religion where any girl who conceived out of wedlock had to either exile herself for a life away in a big city or England - or maybe give birth in secret and hope that such news never leaked out. Invariably it would, and it meant such a woman would never be the same in the eyes of so many 'christians.'

All over Ireland, it was tough to stay on the right side of these Sunday morning juries; mostly the flock just sat there in muted acquiescence with such judgments.

The real sin was that we allowed the church to do our thinking for us and so we weren't really aware that we should question such cold and calculating verdicts.

Events across the decades since those times have shown the church to be cruel, dishonest and hypocritical with the result, thank God, that it has lost that vice-like grip on the minds of communities. Which is not to say that religion, be it Catholic, Protestant or another version, has not been a source of succour to most Irish people, particularly at times of illness and death.

Unfortunately, there were too many times when church and church figures were only interested in keeping people in their place.

I am eternally grateful to three people from those insular times I grew up in who showed enough freedom of spirit to rebel at convention and live by their own different views.

That took real character as the rest of us slavishly adhered to rules designed to keep people in their place both in this life and while they prepared for the next.

## REBEL 1

The first 'rebel' was a man who came to live near us in my pre-teen years. He was enormously popular when he visited our house - until it was time for my father to begin the rosary. Then, he was up and gone before you could shake a beads in front of his nose.

One night when he called early, the chat got round to confessions. It was my father's custom to go every two weeks and he insisted we all did the same. Innocently, he asked our new neighbour how long it was since he was last inside a confessional. He replied matter-of-factly: "The night before I got married."

When it was suggested to him that he 'had' to have an outlet to confess his sins, the man retorted: "He (the priest) doesn't tell me what he does. As soon as he does, I'll tell him what I'm up to."

My father liked the man too much to blacken his name to us but he was genuinely worried that he would end up on the hob of hell if he didn't mend his ways.

This man had this great sense that life was to be enjoyed, unlike many who had it engrained in them that life, on the contrary, was to be feared and endured. He made more people laugh than anyone I knew in that circle which struck me as a much better 'religion' to follow than one where everything was guilt-ridden and sinful or possibly both.

## REBEL 2

Sex, they say, would never have raised its ugly head in Ireland only for Gay Byrne and the Late, Late Show on Saturday nights. Obviously sent to do the devil's work, he was denounced from the pulpit, yet the country tuned in on Friday (and later Saturday) nights without fail to watch the programme.

After one such show, an old farmer from beside us, surprisingly began talking about the taboo subject to us as if he was commenting on the weather.

Better than that, he lifted the lid for my brother and I on how sex had not only survived but thrived despite parish priests riding white horses on maypole nights to ensure no boy and girl walked home in each other's company after such dances.

"The lads who were shy and unable to talk to girls walked home under the priest noses full of piety and virtue. Those of us who wanted action were already doing our best to keep the human race going in the fields," he expounded as he sat on his bike with one leg firmly planted on the ground.

I was probably mid-teens when this man, then probably in his seventies, told tale upon tale of who, what and where these nights of revelry occurred the other side of a ditch as the man of the cloth rode like King William down the highway.

Trying to square the circle of sin in the eyes of an older generation, I asked him if he thought that what was going on was a mortal sin.

He spat, as was his habit before answering: "Well, young lad, you can take this from me," he said. "If that is a sin, then we're all damned."

I was probably a good bit older by the time we got to talk one evening about life, death and immortality. "You know what," he voiced conspiratorially to me. "The nearer I get to dying, the more I believe that when you close your eyes, that's it."

When he died, I attended his funeral and had to fight back laughter when the priest spoke of the great faith of the deceased and how he had lived a simple life only doing God's will.

## REBEL 3

My uncle, who while profoundly religious, had the gumption to take on the upper class of his time, even if it led to his being ostracized from his own by living as an 'exile' in Dublin.

Ultimately, the place we shared as our home,

though half a century apart, wasn't big enough for him and he had to move on. But not before he changed the culture of how the landed gentry treated the ordinary peasant in our locale.

As the third boy in the family, he was down the pecking order in the farm succession stakes. Mostly he eschewed the farmyard chores and responsibilities as his main interest lay in engineering pursuits.

Our neighbour two doors up the road was a recognised genius of all things mechanical in the local jute factory. He was the foreman in the mechanic room and his wife and my grandmother were close friends. When my uncle left school at 14, he was brought into the factory, which at the time employed close to 1,000 people from all over the county, and began to serve his time.

This was his bailiwick and he loved every minute of the learning, particularly the knowledge that his foreman was handing down to him on a daily basis.

He augmented this practical understanding by sending away for books on particular turbines and engines. He had found his calling among his own community and could see his future mapped out for decades ahead.

The neighbour was a tough task-master and rounded on all the young trainees but most particularly my uncle if he made the slightest mistake in the course of his daily duty.

During the years he was learning his trade, it was as if he didn't care or take too much notice. However when he came out of his time and was properly qualified and considered exceptionally good at his job, he found the constant examination of his work a source of irritation.

He decided to turn the tables by fighting the ire he felt with the fun he created by becoming a prankster in the section. A bucket of machine oil set on top of a half opened door fell on the strict neighbour's head as he opened it fully to walk from one workroom to the next.

In an age when the younger workers played football out the back with a ball made up of paper and cloth at break-time, he would prepare one specially, with a large stone inside it, to toss at the neighbour as he emerged for his mid-afternoon smoke.

With my uncle invitingly rolling the ball into his path, the older man couldn't resist having a kick at it. The excruciating pain was immediate on impact, forcing the old man to hobble off on one foot as he tried to soothe the pain in the other by holding it.

The result of that was a work suspension for my uncle and a period on crutches for his foreman.

At home my grandmother was embarrassed on two fronts - her son's reputation now that he was on a last warning in his job and the fact that her relationship with both her neighbour and his wife had become strained.

When he returned to work, he got a hero's welcome from his younger colleagues but he was called into the office where the owner again left him in no doubt as to his future conduct.

He could have been summarily dismissed later that week when the old neighbour mounted his bike to go home for his dinner at one o'clock.

As he began to pick up speed away from the factory, the twine which was tied to his bike became totally taut with the pole it had been tied too fifty yards away, leading to the man heading forward over the handlebars as the bike obeyed the pull of the twine by stopping suddenly.

It didn't take a forensic expert to work out whose hands were all over such a prank - instead the wounded foreman went into our house that night, to bluntly tell my granny that a further indiscretion would end in the sack, regardless of the fact that it was her son.

My granny pleaded with my uncle to behave himself. He promised that he would but there was an inevitability about the ending. The final straw, when it was enacted, came in very peculiar circumstances.

There were two lines of the same family who owned the jute factory and they lived in big houses on either side of the town.

Usually, if a message had to be brought to either home, the owners would go into the mechanic room, instead of the general workers area, to ask one of the mechanics to do the delivery.

On this particular afternoon, my uncle was chosen to go and was on his way around by the lake and into the fields when his attention was drawn by the sound of laughter and female squealing coming from a hayshed up by the woods.

He stole closer to find one of the bosses and a young female in close proximity to each other on the hay. He hung around long enough to know what was happening, before furtively escaping along a track, using the shelter of the trees to ensure he wasn't caught spying. The following day, during an inspection in the mechanic room, the young boss passed a comment on my uncle's work.

"That lathe is not turning the metal as straight as it should," he said, addressing my uncle only by his surname, with a typical air of superiority by that class of that time.

It was a step too far.

"Actually," my uncle snapped back, "it is perfect to the nearest thou." (A 'thou' being to the nearest one-thousand of an inch).

Such insolence could not be tolerated. The young man, dressed immaculately in a three-piece suit, raised his voice as a sign that he would not brook such indiscipline among his workforce. "I'm telling you it is not straight," he said again, this time emphasizing the word 'straight.'

He ordered my uncle to stop work and head to the office to get what he was owed and his qualification papers.

It was the ultimate triumph for a man by now surrounded by an audience and holding all the aces in his hand.

As other men listened in attentively, my uncle rubbed his greased hands in his overalls to clean them before reaching for his coat.

"Your problem is you are not seeing as clearly as normal. Maybe it's because you still have hayseed in your eyes from yesterday," he said with such precision that if his words were darts, they would have all hit the bulls-eye.

The boss blushed profusely at the remark. A few in the background sniggered, and then stifled their laughter in fear of what might happen.

My uncle stared unflinchingly into the eyes of the owner. One of them would have to blink, he knew, but as this was the last day in the factory and in front of his workmates, he decided it wouldn't be him. Finally, the young boss held out his hand and said. "No hard feelings, Joe."

My uncle felt it big of the man, even if it was at the moment he was sacking him. Answering as he shook the other's hand, he said in a strong, clear voice: "None, Eric. Absolutely none."

That encounter was a cameo that defined my uncle's life. "I was the only worker on first name terms with the landed gentry of the town," he would boast to us decades later.

"The only trouble was," he would add with a sense of self-deprecation, "No one would hire me when it got out. I had to leave the town and move to Dublin to earn a living after that."

# 9

# The Robin's Nest

Good years and bad years punctuate the cycle of every farmer's life since time began. More often than not, those years are equally linked to the good or bad weather affecting the outcome of crop yields and also the opportunity to save the hay and other such fodder for livestock during the following winter months.

As a young lad, I can remember older people referencing 1947 – or Black '47 – in every conversation which spoke about tough times on the land.

You didn't have to wait long in my own time for a bad year. I can remember several from the time I was no more than five or six. Then one year when I was a teenager, the spring and early summer became a series of long and wet weeks following each other.

We were behind with the tilling, we were behind with the turf and we were behind with the milk yields to the churn because the grass wasn't growing as well as it would with warmer days to heat it.

In such times, people walked around in a state of gloom because of what they were unable to do due to the weather's influence and, of course, there was always the constant fear that neither the hay nor the barley would be saved at all that year.

In many ways, the Irish summer had a habit of setting riddles to farmers over when to mow meadows or when to cut the corn.

Wet weather retarded the meadows and lodged the barley or wheat in the tilled fields. There were times when we were ordered out into a barley field with four-grain forks to lift the lodged stems from the ground in case they re-sprouted their heads and seriously devalued the crop.

There was a collective to the worry over all these conditions because meals were a time when all the problems of the farm were on the agenda. If a milking bucket was kicked by a cow and needed to be fixed or replaced, that came up immediately as it was only ever a few hours to the next milking.

The state of the land – too wet was bad but too dry and burnt was worse because livestock had less to eat in such circumstances – was always a current topic. Preparing fields to sow and reap crops in was a movable conversation as the months of a given year rolled by.

There was plenty of black humour around when situations went from bad to worse. I remember the year I referred to earlier when so much rain had fallen that we still hadn't a cock of hay cut, never mind saved, by the end of July. It was panic stations not just in our house but in every holding around our area.

At the first sign of the sun there was a stampede to cut the, by then, very thick and 'butty' meadows. This heavy cut resulted in a lot of damage to the machinery – mostly mowing arms – that in turn slowed down the work that needed to be done.

We hired different local contractors to cut our various fields and often had to join a long queue of landowners wanting the same job done at the same time. The size of the demand meant that when the man finally got to your meadow, the weather would have changed back to rain or showers that was far from ideal conditions in which to fell your crop.

Some of our neighbours used to be led and said by the BBC's long-range weather forecast as the one on RTE, or Radio Éireann as it mostly was then, only ever seemed to tell you what the weather was like after it had happened.

In our family, we had our own signs – if the swallows flew low after flies or midges, it augured well but if you saw a dog eating grass, well that was almost definitely a case of further rain on the horizon.

When a day was wet there was always Plan B work to keep a body busy; instead of turning or piking hay, we might be cutting ditches or pulling buachalans (ragworts) or using slash-hooks to knock down thistles which seemed to flourish no matter the weather.

This was soul-destroying work but it had to be done; however, you undertook such chores mindful that the big summer stuff was still waiting over your head like the sword of Damocles. The prolonged foul weather only made sure it would be much harder to do that work whenever the time came.

It was the last day of July when my father employed a great character of a man to cut the meadow. This man didn't like doing the small things in life such as sharpening the blades in his mowing arm behind the grey Ferguson tractor he owned. Instead he would try to use speed to cut the grass.

Now this was worth seeing in itself. The driver would lift the mowing arm, reverse maybe 20 yards and then go forward at high speed. Then, just as he arrived at where the uncut meadow was he would push down the hydraulic to drop the arm and use the velocity he had generated to get him another 10 or 15 yards on with his cut. By then, it would have clogged up again and I was deployed to take the grass away from the choked-up fingers – dangerous, particularly if he inadvertently switched the power back to the blade.

In an effort to improve the situation, my father returned home to search his box of tools and brought back a whetstone and a metal sharpener. Then he began the laborious task of sharpening each blade so that the contractor could do the work properly.

That said, it was far from being the most unpleasant hour he had ever spent as the man whose implements he was working on was a great storyteller. As well as enjoying the story, he would often have himself as the butt of the joke, which endeared him even further to his listeners.

He was the first one I remember who ever told a story about sex in which my father and myself were the listeners. Instead of using textbook terms such as sexual intercourse, he brought the agricultural terminology of 'tipping' in its stead. I ended up falling around as he produced the punch line on the slightly crude story but was more surprised to see my father – a man who never used the F-word in his life – enjoying the banter.

My father had a great rapport with the man and advised him that he would be much better off taking the time to have his implements in proper working order rather than trying "to bull" his way through the work.

The man agreed between puffs on his cigarette but you sensed he had no time for such menial chores. It was evident though that he was delighted to have my father work on the blades. Properly sharpened, the man swept through the meadows in the 'three-fields' triangle of land much quicker than appeared possible when he first began.

It was a calculated risk by my father to put so much hay on the flat at one given time; it meant that if we didn't get the weather, we would have the bulk of our winter fodder in peril of either not being made at all or being of such poor quality to be virtually worthless.

Normally after the cutting was done by a contactor with a tractor, we had the mare to row the hay with the gig-rake and bring it in to the cocks in the field with the timber paddy-rake.

That year the mare was slightly lame and the contractor said he would get a loan of a turner for the tractor and do that job for us. He came back a few days later when the grass had changed from green to a better hay colour of light brown and rowed the swathes for us in his own inimitable way.

We would usually first turn the swathes individually, then row them together in twos that allowed the grass to be fluffed up as part of the airing and drying process.

This man went the whole hog and put four swathes into each row – meaning it would take twice as long to dry out if it was to be right for piking (cocking).

There was no need to tempt fate that year – fate was on the ball writing its own script. No sooner had the contractor left the fields with this new arrangement of big rows thrown together than the heavens opened and it continued to pour down for over a week.

I've seldom seen my father express so much worry in his face as after his daily visit to check on the condition of the meadow in the 'three-fields.'

"The grass is growing up through them big rows now, it will be like saving dung the way the weather has turned against us," he said one evening when we were eating our supper after we had finished the milking.

I had mixed feelings over the hay that year; on one hand I knew we would have to face into it sometime and dig up the rows from the grass growing through them which would be a nightmare. On the other hand, the on-going rain meant we could often doss around the house or the yard with no work schedule planned which normally would not happen if we were gone to the fields for the day.

Inevitably, the bad spell broke around the middle of the month and then it was a case of all hands on deck – that meant my father, my brother and myself.

Fate turned the weather from being wet and cool into a period of intense heat from the sun which delivered a 'closeness' and heaviness about the day that you would have offered a king's ransom after an hour's work just to feel the lightest of breezes on your cheeks.

Where each turning of a field would normally take a few hours when we rowed the hay ourselves, we were now taking an hour just to go round the outside three lanes – so entangled was the hay with the growth up through it. Every sweep of the fork was met with the stout resistance of the new grass that had become embroidered and embedded into it.

Turning the hay was usually easy and quite pleasant. You could count your progress by the different colours the hay just turned appeared against the paler hues of those that were yet to be touched.

This particular year, every time you used the fork you had to shake it through; after a short while the arms ached at all the extra effort that was required to 'dig' the hay out from where it lay.

By late evening and with only a few quick breaks for food, we had managed to turn every blade in the 12 acres in those fields surrounded by high ditches.

That extra shelter made it close to sweatshop working conditions. Or as my father put it: "There isn't a breath of air to be had here today."

The following day was another scorcher and my father said that if we turned the rows back to where they were lying the previous day, we might manage the impossible – and save the hay.

He believed that while there was no doubt it

would not be top quality, it would improve and could yet be of sufficient value to keep the cattle going for the winter.

As we went about doing the very opposite of our work from the previous day, I remember thinking how this must be the mindless sort of work prisoners are given just to pass their time.

I envisaged seeing a jailer with a megaphone telling the inmates: "Bring that load of sand over to the other side of the compound". And then when they had completed the chore, he would tell them: "Now bring it back again."

The numbness of this work, allied to the flies eating our faces, meant that the thought of a swim at our tea-break was what kept my brother and myself going. "Swim" was probably a bit too grandiose a term for what we did as there was a tiny rivulet – called The Little River – at the edge of our fields which was seldom more than eighteen inches deep in summertime.

However it was always cold as ice and after three hours working under the sun, had wonderful restorative qualities.

All we did was strip off to our pants, jump in, thrash around for 30 seconds and then dry ourselves with the shirts we had discarded and would use as damp clothing for the afternoon session. That way we killed two birds with one stone to fight against the conditions.

The third day was even hotter still and as we finished the milking, my father went up to the Church Field to catch the mare for the day's work ahead. He planned to use the gig-rake to change where the rows lay, thus putting them on fresh ground as part of 'rearing' the hay back to good health. That, he claimed, would give whatever air was there the chance to get through the hay and improve it further before we began the piking work.

My brother and myself were inside having the breakfast when he came in. "We've a problem lads," he said. "There's a robin after building her nest in the horse's collar."

The mare had been having something of a holiday that summer with the bad weather and being lame and her harnesses were put by in a shed to keep them dry. No one had been in there for a few weeks except for the robin, which obviously saw it as an ideal place to plan the hatching and raising of a family.

I thought that robins only built their nests in spring but my father told us they would often have two or three broods in the one year. Maybe the weather had a bearing on the lateness of this brood, but when the robin flew off its nest on my father's entry to the shed, there were five little eggs there still waiting to be hatched. I was sure that being a practical man, he would take the nest out of the collar, lay it somewhere else in the shed and hope the mother would continue with her hatching.

"That won't happen. If you interfere with the nest, she will abandon it and the chicks will die," he explained matter-of-factly.

I was about to say a big "so what" when he continued. "It's never lucky or right to do that to nature," he said firmly. "We'll see if we can borrow a collar or if not, sure thank God we have the use of our limbs to do the work."

He dispatched me to three neighbours who, like himself, farmed with the horse instead of the tractor. I was back within the hour reporting that all of them were out saving hay like ourselves. I was ashamed to tell those farmers' wives the real reason our horse's collar was out of commission, saying that it had come apart when we tried to put it on the mare that morning.

It was close to midday when we began doing the horse's work ourselves. I was really unhappy at the way fortune had played its hand to keep us working like animals but there was no alternative once my father had decided not to interfere with the laws of nature, as he saw it.

It was slow and monotonous trying to carry forkfuls of hay from 10 or 20 yards away to where a particular cock was being made. After a while, necessity became the mother of invention and my brother and I worked in tandem to roll big swathes of hay into where my father was expertly shaping the cock.

By late afternoon, we were close to finishing the first field. As we sat drinking our mugs of tea under the beech tree for a rest, I noticed Darkie, our dog, eating grass.

"Rain on the way," I shouted. "Look at Darkie with the grass."

My father scanned the skyline. "Rain might be coming but it won't be here until tomorrow by the look of the sky. We can pike the lot if we keep going till dark."

"Ah beautiful," I thought to myself. "Even the lads in Mountjoy now enjoy better conditions than us."

I laughed out loud at the thought. Black humour has its grains of sustenance for us all. My father looked over at me and wondered if I was alright in the head. At that moment, he had a point.

We were moving into the second field when we got a boost at the sight of one of the neighbour's arriving with his horse and a paddy-rake. He had finished piking his field and like neighbours of the time, knew there wouldn't be too many spare horse's collars available on the day. As if providence felt it had mocked us long enough, no sooner had he begun to bring the hay in and triple the pace of our work than our cousins arrived miraculously armed with enough forks to form a battalion in a civil war militia.

My spirits soared. With eight men and my aunt working, we broke up into three separate gangs with my father, my uncle and my aunt the anchors as we began attacking the fields, three cocks at a time.

By six o'clock we were in the back-field and the rate of our progress had every one of us in good form. As the angelus sounded, we all stopped to pray, then the elders had a smoke and my aunt insisted my cousin and I relight a fire so that we could have a cup of tea to look forward to within the hour.

By the time we had the tea ready and my aunt had dished out the scones she had brought with her, we were on the last lap.

The last round-up of work was at the far end where the grass had been most stubborn in drying out but which was now in as ideal condition as it ever would be.

Seldom have I felt such euphoria like that evening after saving the hay in the three fields, going home happy to milk the cows and then to complete the other chores.

That night, as my brother and I sat down to watch television, there was that wonderful sense of joy at the achievement of having successfully completed a major farm task.

We had worked two 16-hour days and it was mid-morning the following day when I emerged from the greatest sleep of my life.

As I dressed myself, I could hear the tinkling of rain into the barrels below and knew from the conversation coming from the kitchen that my father and brother were having breakfast following the milking.

"Here's sleepy head," said my brother as I joined them at the table and began pouring a cup of tea.

I grunted and pointed at my father to pass the bread and the butter.

"Before you sit down," he said in that lovely tone he would use when he had a pleasant surprise in store. "Go down to the horse's collar. It'll do your heart good."

I did as he asked and as I opened the door, the robin flew out of the nest. There nestling snugly were five little chicks. Within a minute, the mother was back again, unafraid at my presence and with a supply of food in her mouth to give to her little 'uns.

When I went back inside to the kitchen, my father looked at me for reaction.

I nodded back to him, saying "five chicks."

"Five chicks," he repeated as he slugged down the last of his tea.

Of course it was more than just about five chicks. It was my father's understanding of life and how it should be lived. That morning, he was passing it on for us to follow.

# 10

# The Abattoir

Adults in the country were by nature very protective of children particularly when it came to the more unsightly aspect of living on the land.

I was never allowed into the yard if a heifer or cow was being serviced by the local bull. Similarly if my father was castrating calves or lambs, we were invariably sent to herd cattle or rise water in some remote part of the farm while the other chore was carried out.

Bringing a heifer or lambs to the local abattoir attached to the butcher's shop was another such occasion when our helping hands were passed over.

Indeed my parents had a simple rule of having the animals collected while we were at school, thus avoiding the drama of sadness and tears which would have accompanied their final journey – had we known about it.

The year after I received my first holy communion I gave my father two shillings to mark his birthday on the second last day of the year – December 30.

That spring we had a clutch of triplets from the ewes and I had been given one as a pet. He was reared on a bottle and lived in the tea-chest inside our kitchen – and as far as I was concerned he was one of the family.

However one day when I arrived home to find that he had suddenly disappeared, something told me he wasn't coming back.

No one definitively said that he had gone to the butchers but I blamed my father for whatever had happened. I felt I owed it to the departed lamb to ask for my two shillings back.

A few years after all that rancour had passed into the forgotten chambers of memory, something strange happened one day on the way home from school.

It was a Friday evening and the teacher had allowed us off half an hour early because we had stayed quiet when he left for an hour to go to a funeral.

On the way up the main street with my cousin and my friend from the town, we became aware of a hullabaloo around The Square.

A heifer that a farmer had brought into the butcher's for killing had escaped from the abattoir and was heading our way. The townspeople, unused to the vagaries of animals, fled into shop doorways for safety to shelter from this mini-Pamplona scene being played out before their eyes – with just one animal.

My friend also ducked into a hallway but my cousin and I, as if by reflex action, stuck out our arms and turned the animals back up the street.

As we did so, the farmer and the man from the abattoir came into view, spluttering and coughing following their enforced run after the animal.

The four of us chaperoned the beast as far as the butcher's side-gate and then closed it so that the heifer couldn't escape a second time.

As the man went inside to get his money in the butcher's stall, myself and my cousin hung around to see if we could get any more of the action that might follow – we had, after all, half an hour of time to play with before heading home to begin our daily work after school.

The butcher's assistant – a kindly man – thanked us for helping him with the beast and then invited us in to watch her being slaughtered.

"Stand behind that barrier over there so that you don't get hurt," he said, pointing to a place in the abattoir which was safe from animals.

He led the heifer into a makeshift crush and then

forced her head into a brace which left her powerless as he prepared to put a bullet in her head.

"Watch her now," he said with what I detected was a sense of regret. "These poor devils have a sixth sense and seem to know that they are going to die."

As if to emphasise his point, the heifer bucked and tried to escape the clutches of the bars which kept her head rigid within the tight crush.

Then she began to bawl – a low lowing that seemed to come from the very core of her insides.

She was making a final play for life and I could no longer watch the inevitable that was about to be played out. Feeling responsible to some extent for getting her back into the abattoir following her botched attempt at escape, I wanted to cry but having forced myself into the situation, I had no choice but to stick it out.

The animal's eyes were full of fire – her legs danced up and down as she explored every avenue for a weakness in the defences of the crush. Her sense told her it was now or never.

The butcher's assistant aimed the gun at the back of her head between her ears and fired; her legs immediately gave way but she continued to make exaggerated movements, as if trying from muscle-memory to regain her stance.

He waited patiently above her like an assassin, his arm outstretched with the gun; then when she stilled for a moment, he pulled the trigger again and this time she collapsed in a heap like a pack of cards.

The man surveyed her, rubbed his nose with the sleeve of his overalls, then rubbed his eyes as if he was wiping back tears.

"Go home now, lads," he urged us softly. "I have to cut this poor thing up and the smell will be fierce. Anyway, I think the pair of you have seen enough for one day."

In that moment, I felt a little like the heifer moments earlier as I lost control over my leg movements. My cousin opened the door hurriedly and made his way up the laneway; eventually I followed him, though I was still more than a little unsteady on my legs and queasy in my gut.

When we got up onto the main street, I noticed my cousin was as white as a sheet and was looking as upset as I felt.

Instinctively we both began running. It was now late and we had time to make up.

We ran faster and faster side by side without looking at each other. Our schoolbags shook violently from side to side on our backs, the crayons and pens rattling in their containers.

When we arrived at the hill before his house we both sat down on the side of the road. Aside from the heavy breathing from our exertions, we stayed silent.

Then after what seemed an age, he stood up.

I did the same.

It would be a long evening and longer night. Already the sound the heifer made and the pleading in her eye haunted my thoughts.

I knew my cousin was thinking the same thing. That day at the abattoir was something that affected us both for a long time – so much so that neither of us ever spoke of the slaughter again.

# 11

# The First Of
# The Heroes

They say you should never meet your heroes – and I think there is some truth in that old saying, though there are always exceptions to every rule.

There are different types and levels of heroes – faraway ones like movie stars or soccer players. Gaelic football and hurling is different in that it presents people with a choice – a thing called a local hero.

I was four years old going on five when our county reached its first All-Ireland senior football final. I didn't know then what they really meant but because everyone kept talking about it, I could feel it was more important than saving the barley or even work itself for a time in the late summer/early autumn of 1961.

It was one thing to be from that county and have the player captaining your team with land straight across from us on the other side of the river. What was doubly intriguing was the fact that the captain, the goalkeeper, had an older brother who was considered the best player in Ireland by all the grown-ups yet the county board had decided not to bring him home from New York to play in that game.

While the captain was a hero on our headlands and cross-roads and through the streets of our town, his brother took on almost mystical status in our group of First Infants in school as the Franciscan monks spoke to us about how these brothers had brought fame and glory on the little holdings which made our cluster of neighbours and friends.

One teacher spoke of seeing him kick a ball 50 yards into the wind in a provincial match for the county, "and the ball was only rising as it went over the bar," he added.

Those two brothers did indeed bring great pride and honour to their own, who for weeks before the final and years afterwards spoke of the game as if it was more important than the Berlin Wall, which as it happened was erected around the same time.

They began building it in August of that year – 1961 – and the authorities claimed it was to keep anti-fascist influences from getting into East Germany, the reality was it stopped their own people from fleeing the Soviet-dominated East German government regime.

My father's trimmings had already included "Three Hail Marys for Matt Talbot, Fr Willie Doyle and the conversion of Russia."

Both events were added to the rosary at night. As our county was playing its semi-final game, this became an added trimming – three Hail Marys that the county would win. When that happened there was three more that the final would also have a favourable outcome.

As the communists partitioned Berlin, there was no doubt about whose side the man above was on, yet the real and present fear among the local people was that those non-believers would take over the rest of Europe and persecute us for our religious beliefs and way of life.

One neighbour went so far as to say he would rather face 'The Balubas' from Africa than the sort of atheism which was in danger of taking off behind the Berlin Wall. We grew up familiar with that term – because of the Niemba Ambush which took place the previous year.

An Irish platoon in the Congo on a peacekeeping mission was ambushed by this tribe, who used among other weapons poisoned darts. Nine Irish soldiers died among the heavy casualties of that encounter. From the sadness of the Balubas massacre and the fear of the Berlin Wall, the county's march to the All-Ireland gave the people something positive and uplifting on which to dwell.

Long before the game was played, one man, who worked for my uncle, proclaimed that the county would rue the day it didn't bring our neighbour home to mark the other county's danger man. We couldn't possibly win without him, he stressed.

His view wasn't fully appreciated in the optimism before the game but afterwards when most believed the absent player would indeed have changed the outcome, his prescience elevated him in everyone's regard.

Mindful that there was no RTE television in Ireland at that juncture – it arrived some months later – the match was 'watched' by most people on radios, except for the large crowd who boarded the train to take them to Dublin for the encounter.

At least those who attended could claim to be part of a historical fact which has survived to this day – the 90,556 at the '61 football final was and is the largest crowd ever to have attended a final in the history of the GAA.

The disappointment of losing by a point in such a great game was something that was tempered by the fact that the county had come so close in its first ever appearance in an All Ireland final.

The players and especially the captain were welcomed home as heroes by the neighbours and friends who felt sure that they would bring home the Sam Maguire the following year.

The build up to the match and the excitement among the monks allowed discipline to slacken as classes were allowed out to the field to play games as if it was the pupils who were playing in Croke Park.

There was a return to normality the following week. One monk had taped the All-Ireland and got permission to play it to all the classes from the principal after he had edited it all together. We loved the break – anything was better than having Irish beaten into our thick skulls.

I don't know why I didn't listen to the game on Radio Éireann because we had a set in our house – my guess is that I would have been playing cowboys and indians with my cousins and that would have been more important to a four or five year old than sitting with grown ups on a Sunday afternoon for over an hour around the radio.

The monk who played the radio recording had the best technology of the time but still had to stop several times to spool on other tapes which were needed to cover the entire game on his large recording machine.

I remember nothing about the scores or scorers, only the commentator's voice and the ultimate pall of sadness that descended at the realisation that we had lost and our neighbour would not get the opportunity to bring home the cup.

'Imagine lads if he had won, he would surely have brought it in here," said the Franciscan brother, making the gloom even heavier at the thought.

He may have thought that it could happen the following year like others had said but next year didn't come in that context for the county and indeed when the first All Ireland was finally won a decade later, only one player from '61 was still starting on the county team.

Ireland, then as now, exported many of its finest people in search of work and in time our captain followed his brother to the shores of America. Almost immediately, those brothers made their name playing in the New York colours at a time in the sixties when that city could compete with the great three-in-a-row Galway side and others by beating them over two legs in the National League finals.

Other than the time of that particular All Ireland final, my father had little or no time for the GAA. It obviously rubbed off on me then as even in school, I hadn't any interest and didn't stay behind to train for the school teams like others in my class.

One day near the time of our summer holidays, our teacher decided not to do any formal classwork but instead divided us up into two teams of 15 and play a match which he came out to referee.

When I picked up the ball off the ground early on as it rolled in my direction he admonished me loudly in front of all the others: "Listen, you clown, put your foot under the ball."

When he called me over after the game, I thought it was to follow on with his criticism of my display. Instead he was complimentary. "If you got a bit of coaching, you could make the under-twelves next year," he said. "See if your parents will give you permission to come back after school for practice."

It was at the time my mother had been diagnosed with cancer and was in hospital virtually all the time. My father was away quite a bit from home down where our land was so it meant I could go back to train without worrying that he would find out.

Over the following year or so I improved with practice as the Brother had predicted and actually came to enjoy playing Gaelic football. We won the county schools championship – it seemed most of the boys on the team had parents there for the final while neither of mine, for different reasons, even knew I was playing.

Some months later my mother died and life went on, as it does. We adapted to the loss though it was years before I went a day without feeling diminished by her absence. Football gave me an interest outside of the farm and school and in many ways it was the crutch I grasped to help me through.

Some years later when I was playing for one of the GAA underage teams, we learned that the captain of the '61 All Ireland winning team was home from

America. Most of the lads on this team were old enough to know who he was and what he had achieved on the pitch both here and in New York.

We trembled at the thought of meeting our own celebrity. He shook hands with all the boys, smiling, asking our names and quizzing each of us on our families. When he came to me I was tongue-tied, such was the awe I felt in his presence. It took the intervention of one of our mentors to tell him my name and who my parents were.

The smile disappeared off his face and he clasped me by the shoulder and held my hand tightly before speaking into my ear.

"I was so sorry to hear about your mother. The good die young," he said as he gave me a nod of clear understanding.

He then shook his head and a look of sadness crossed his countenance. I didn't know it then but later it was pointed out to me that his mother too had died when he was young.

Of all the condolences I got as a child on her loss, his is the only one that has stuck with me to this day, that handshake, that look of empathy in his face – truly a hero who hadn't forgotten his own.

# 12

# The Solitary Life

Other than the fact that he had enquired at one time if my aunt would be interested in marrying him, I knew nothing about this man.

No one did.

It seems that after her rebuttal, he withdrew as much as he could from the prospect of family life.

While he could be classed as a neighbour because he lived along the route we travelled every day bringing cows to and from our farm, in truth, I knew as much about the man in the moon as I did about him.

All I could tell you now is that he lived alone – and

he died alone. In his later life, I think I remember a relative calling periodically to see him but other than that no one, save for the postman, darkened his door.

He was quiet and he was gentle – you could see kindness in his expression and in his eyes in particular – but beyond that this man had little intrusion in my life.

In early summer, I would see him with his old donkey cutting turf in what I thought was a good field of his, one which he should have kept for grazing instead of using to save his winter fuel. I felt like saying that to him when I walked the road behind our cows and had a minute to pass the time of day. He didn't encourage chat. His wave of recognition was a greeting of sorts but also a sign to say the communication was ending.

On those days, he still wore the hat that was part of his being but stripped down to his waistcoat and at times when the weather was really warm, to an old-fashioned blue-lined, collarless white shirt.

His house had a similar modesty about it – it's gable end at right angles to the road defending the rest of its structure to the casual human gaze from along the road.

He did his work diligently and without anyone ever hearing the sound of his raised voice.

On the bike to and from town to get his messages, he was deferential, doffing his hat to any woman he encountered along the way and smiling at the likes of me to recognise us without partaking in conversation.

My uncles and father liked the man and often praised him for the way he kept his fields and went about his work.

There is no earthly reason that this man should be so much part of my thoughts several decades after he has passed on to his eternal reward. Yet his soft face, and even softer voice lives inside my head.

It forces me to think of him and the life he could have had if he had married my aunt. For starters, he would have had all of us trafficking in and out of his homestead visiting her, perhaps playing with his offspring – children who I know he would have loved and cherished for he had a demeanour of gentleness.

That house of his which could have resounded to so much happiness and life, instead has stood sentry over a nothingness for decades and will remain so until in time, it caves in on itself.

The footsteps he placed on this earth may have disappeared but he walks my mind as vividly as if he just passed me on the roadway half an hour ago.

When he joins my inner person it seems to be with a lesson to seize the day as it comes, to play the hand you're dealt or otherwise yours will be the life of a loner.

His offer of marriage had been through a third

party, and the decline had been brought back to him through the same source.

I was with my aunt only once, walking up the street to her house, when he happened to pass us on his bicycle.

"Evenin' Mam, young fella," he said warmly, without showing any further interest in us.

My aunt used his name to reply in a friendly tone. Maybe, years before, if he had plucked up the courage to get down off his bike and ask her out, his and her history would have had a different ending.

Instead, he played out the role of the solitary man, with thousands like him in the Ireland of that time.

# 13

# The Worst Job On The Farm

The day was hot and humid. It felt like someone had just opened a window on a big outdoor oven and a blast of heat had hit us straight in the face.

Everything was hiding on the farm except the flies and bugs that were airborne and intent on buzzing around the heads of animals and humans.

The cattle had taken refuge amid the branches under the trees – there they avoided the direct rays of the sun and the torment of the flies which found it harder to navigate among the leaves and branches.

The mare and pony also had their heads in the leaves under the big tree – and each had a way of shaking their skin to dislodge the horseflies that appeared to be everywhere.

My brother and myself were out in the middle of the field rounding up the sheep. We had the job of herding them and having taken the lazy way out for the previous week, were now feeling guilty as my father's inspection on this day had sensed maggots in the flock.

For sure, it was 'maggot weather'. Earlier as we were passing up to another field he had seen one of the lambs trying to bite back at her hind area – a real sign that it was infested with those parasites.

We were starting out on this chore on the backfoot; his tone clearly indicated disapproval that we hadn't detected this problem during the week. He had entrusted us with the responsibility of counting and examining them and we hadn't done that.

Of course he was perfectly right to be annoyed but when you are teenagers, the lazy way out – by looking across the ditch and doing a head count seemed good enough for us.

Every walk of life has at least one part of it that is universally hated – and taking maggots out of a sheep's fleece was the one on the farm. The very thought of it turned my stomach; the smell up close was one thing but the sight of the little clusters of cream parasites pulsing into the flesh of the sheep was even more repulsive.

We didn't have a pin or crush in any of our fields to usher animals into for examination in such circumstance. At that time, we had only one choice – round up the sheep and hem them into a corner of the field from which they could not escape.

When that was achieved, we would identify the ewe or lamb we wanted to look at. One of us would volunteer to steal in among the flock to catch the suffering animal. As we did so, the others would dash left, right and centre in fear as they tried to escape our clutches and run back up the field.

Sometimes if we failed on the first attempt to catch the one we wanted, we would have to go back out and together with the dogs drive them back into the particular corner from which they could not break out.

My father had really big and strong hands – when he clutched something, it stayed clutched. I didn't possess anything like the same strength and there were times when I would insist on going in to catch the sheep – get a grip on the fleece but ultimately fail to hold on to the scared animal.

This day I'm referring to became memorable for all the wrong reasons. As we drove the sheep into a corner, we noticed that not just one or two but actually three lambs had black areas around their hindquarters. That meant we needed to catch and examine all three. So we decided that each one of us would identify one of the maggoty lambs and then take the responsibility of catching and holding on to them.

As we closed in, the sheep became exceedingly nervous and were looking for gaps in our defence to get away. The two dogs patrolled behind us like fullbacks ready to mop up anything which might breach the half-back line. The sheep could see that we had set up well defensively which forced them to pack tighter and tighter together. A few even jumped up on one another in their efforts to get further away from us.

Then at my father's signal, the three of us attacked, each with his eyes on the one designated to him. My father was clinical; like an old assassin, he was in and had his quarry off its front legs in an instant as he dragged the lamb out into the clearing; my brother's initial attempt to swoop and conquer was thwarted when he tripped over the dog as he tried to step sideways to block off a possible exit path. His lamb, with an outrageous side-step like a tricky Gaelic or rugby player, wrong-footed him and looked to have made good its escape.

However just when all seemed lost, my brother somehow managed to dive back-ways and as if he had eyes in the back of his head, expertly wrestled his lamb to the ground and managed to hold onto him.

While all this was happening in a time frame of no more than a few seconds, I went in pursuit of the lamb with the greatest amount of dirty dags –

knowing by the visual examination that his would be the worst case to be looked at.

In our family, we had a pecking order in terms of who did what job. Without doubt, if there was only one sheep requiring attention, my brother or I would have done the catching but my father would be the one to probe for the worms and then dislodge them with a wrist movement of his right hand reminiscent of a banjo player strumming his instrument.

This was a first; all three of us had lambs in our possession. So whether we were good at it or not, it was up to each of us to carry out his own examination.

My father seemed to have no problem squishing the maggots with his hands and he dislodged them with expert wristy-flicks through the infected area.

"Once you dislodge them, they will never reconnect," he reassured us as he opened a large bottle of diluted Jeyes Fluid which he had prepared earlier. He daubed it into the area where the maggots had nested and then threw the disinfectant down the back of the animal and ended by rubbing the liquid into the fleece .

My brother had a real aversion to this chore. Watching him close his eyes and also strum the tail-end area as he held his breath was funny as maggots sprayed up into the air before falling in white heaps onto the ground. My father handed him the Jeyes Fluid bottle and he too ducked the liquid into the charred fleece. When he released his animal, it shook its pelt before wandering off to join up with the rest of the flock.

My quarry wriggled incessantly under the weight of my knee on its midriff as I held its hind legs in my hands after pinning it to the ground. My problem was that every time I tried to free one hand to pull back its wool and probe the skin, it sensed it could escape and began wriggling in the hope of getting back to its feet.

When my father was finished with his lamb, he came over and put his hand under the animal's head, half-paralysing it in the process.

"Go ahead," he said to me, "Check her out for those dirty yokes."

I could almost detect a glint in his eye; he was testing to see if I was up to such a task. I presume I made a disapproving face at the prospect but then decided I wouldn't let myself down by refusing to carry out the sordid work.

I closed my nostrils and began using my right hand to sort through the jagged cluster of dirty wool which we call 'daggins'.

Down by the lambs kidneys, I opened back a parcel of matted wool to discover the first nest of maggots. It wasn't the first time I had seen them but I still felt sick at having to touch them in order to dislodge them.

Aware that the longer I waited the harder such a chore became, I dug my four fingers into the area and immediately the maggots began falling like a burst bag of long-grain rice.

My father was disgusted, not so much at the sight, but the fact that the maggots had eaten so far down into the animal. It suggested neglect to him; we as their shepherds hadn't watched over our sheep and noticed the problems earlier than this.

"It might be too late for this one," he said with a sense of anger in his voice. "The maggots have done a right job on her."

It took us ages firstly to get rid of the parasites, then to cut the daggins off her and finally to rinse her with Jeyes Fluid. By the time we had finished, his judgement was more favourable.

"I'd say we caught her just in time," he ventured.

We did.

Thereafter, although we knew it was the worst job on the farm, we kept a keen eye on the sheep at those times and conditions when they were most likely to have maggots. If we had lost that lamb, the truth is we would never have heard the end of it.

# 14

# Turf Times

**P**AST
Farmers' sons had one advantage over townies – at certain times of the year; they could get a day off to help with various chores on the land.

It might be the threshing if it was September and the wheat or barley was then only ripe enough to cut or in late spring it more often than not was the turf cutting and later on the footing – a very important part of Irish rural life.

My cousin and myself had made ourselves almost indispensable at harvest time in the way we bagged the corn and made sure we dumped them off the side of the Combine Harvester along a line – making it easier for the grown ups to collect them in the tractor and trailer later in the day.

Work on the bog was different – it required stronger types and our brothers, who were both older, usually got the day off school ahead of us.

The status quo in this regard would have remained except the two oldest lads were sent away to boarding school and this time my cousin and myself were given the day off but told in no uncertain terms that we had to step up to the plate.

My father and my uncle and Charlie, the workman for my uncle, were expert sléansmen; we were cast in the role of general helpers, catching the newly cut sods, putting them on the bog buggies and then carting them out to where there was grass so that they could dry.

By the end of the day you had done so much back-breaking work that you wondered would it not have been easier, after all, to put on your good clothes and just go to school.

The bog work was constant at this time of year – after the cutting came the footing, then the stacking or stucking as it was known. Later, in summer, it was all hands on deck to bring home the fuel so that a household was guaranteed warmth for the winter ahead.

Although nominally a hired hand, Charlie often played the role of boss in these situations – particularly in laying down the law to us 'the young fry' about the work pattern of the day.

"There'll be no tea made here till six o'clock this evening," he would declare as we landed down at the bog bank around midday, our parents having firstly done the morning chores before heading off for this annual chore.

Only my aunt would cross his dictats but on this day she had stayed at home and neither my uncle nor my dad said anything.

It turned out the men had worked so hard and so well on the first day that by three o'clock it was Charlie who said to my cousin and I to go find some dry sticks so that we could begin the process of boiling a kettle.

Within half an hour and several hours ahead of what he had initially forecast, we were all seated around the bog barrows drinking tea and eating whatever savoury food had been packed for us.

By six o'clock, we were getting ready to go home. The men were happy we had done a good day's shift in getting the sods out where they could dry on the upland area and praised us for being careful in the way we turned over the buggies.

## PRESENT

There is still a chill of quiet on a bog land you cannot experience anywhere else on this planet and in May this year, I watched the new way of cutting turf for the first time.

My brother and I – some two score years and a bit

after using our hands to catch every sod thrown at us by either our uncle or our father – watched with slight amusement as the man with the big machine began his work. Our cousins had told us he was coming and wondered did we want to cut some turf on a piece of bog we owned adjacent to where we used to cut all those years ago.

We thought it would be good for the soul if not the back just to experience a day on the bog – one more time.

It's no longer a case of boy power or man power but multi horse power as the man's machine sucks up the bog into a hopper and then squeezes the turf material out the back in one long sausage line. You pay for this service by the hopper load – this year it cost €55 per hopper or €440 for the amount we got.

My cousin worked out that for that outlay, and obviously whatever hours were required to rear the turf and get it home – we would own over €2,000 worth of heating material for the winter. Not bad, at least in theory.

## PAST

The only other material which went into our fireplace was whatever timber we cut down around our fields. It was the same across the country as most farmers, and in particular my father, banned briquettes which had become popular from the sixties in town grates.

It would rankle with my father if my mother bought bales of these briquettes behind his back. "You might as well do the decent thing and throw money into the fire as those, because they burn out in minutes," he said a thousand times.

The fact that they threw out more heat and did so much quicker meant my mother always had a stash hidden under the stairs or somewhere outside his line of vision. She worked on the premise that what he didn't know, didn't bother him, particularly when it came to things he considered a waste of money.

The footing and later stacking, or rising of the turf up was quasi ceremonial in the way there were rules to be followed – four sods up on their sides, two on top of those and one on top. That allowed the wind to get in around their flanks and dry them so that they would be fit for stacking.

**PRESENT**

In an era where information is all around, sometimes the occasion of misinformation can be astounding. For instance, my cousin who was doing the turf with us did work on spreading the four hoppers on one side of the road, thinking that what was on the other side was for a friend of ours.

We, on the other hand, had not made any arrangement with this friend and so were disappointed in late July when making the journey down for a funeral to find that the turf 'sausages' were as the man with the machine had laid them out on that side of the makeshift road.

In that period from early May, it was fortunate that the weather had been exceptionally fine, otherwise the sausages would have been pounded back into the earth from which they came.

By the time I got down to start footing the turf, most of my neighbours had saved theirs and indeed many of them had already brought their crops home.

I felt slightly ashamed as I began bending over the first rows of clods at a time when those drawing their turf home looked at us bemused, obviously wondering where we had been until this time of year. Compounding our problems with the delay was the fact that grass had grown up between the rows, making it tough to pull the turf out of the ground.

While it was all down on the ground, the top half of virtually every row was ready to throw in the fire, so good had the weather and drying been. However the lower half was still very much like half-set jelly and was extremely cool and moist to my bare hands.

If you threw that part in the fire, it would put it out rather than add to the flames.

In the new 'sausage era' of turf cutting, it is up to those footing the crop to decide on the length of each 'sod'. Whereas the sleán in the old days gave a squarer sod, now they are manufactured longer – more swiss roll than batchloaf if you like.

Within an hour the fingers on both my hands were in pieces – the hard bits on the top of the turf were like concrete and each time I met resistance pulling them up through the grass, they tore at my finger tops, eventually drawing blood in six of the ten digits.

I also had forgotten the angle you need to set yourself at for this type of work. For someone with a discectomy operation already performed on my back, I've always tried to be careful of how I go about servile work – the odd time I do it anymore.

I managed to prevent my back from going into spasm – the first sign that pain was on the way, but I was nearly locked at a 45 degree angle as I worked frantically towards finding the last sod.

There were three of us at the work, my wife, my youngest son and I. We attacked the rows from different sides and angles and in just under three hours, we had the four hoppers of turf in their first phase of recovery towards becoming genuine fire material for winter warmth.

The bog tests you with its work – there is no hiding place as every hard hour you put in, the reward is there for your eye to see. Similarly every minute or hour you idle or take it easy, it shows in the lesser amount of ground covered around you.

After two hours of constant graft, I could see we all had made headway. There comes a time, and we had reached it, when you need to make a call about how long you plan to keep going.

Used properly, bog psychology works to your advantage but if you fail to press the right buttons with your co-workers, spirits can begin to flag very visibly.

My aunt was arguably the greatest psychologist I ever came across. She could read us all like books. Sometimes when we were getting slightly contrary with our lot as we faced into hours upon uninterrupted hours of further work, she would straighten herself up and say: "Aren't we lucky to be on the high bog today, sure the air here is better than Salthill (Galway)".

At that time we had never been to the acclaimed holiday spot in the West but she had a way in one sentence of making us feel privileged to be there with her in the bogs of middle Ireland.

I was reminded of my aunt as my own spirits began to flag and I heard myself say – "We'll finish up in 20 minutes regardless of what's left because we've done some serious work here today. And sure it's hard work but at least we've had the benefit of fresh air which they say is better than Salthill."

My wife groaned at the comparison and my son didn't respond, but I knew the 20 minutes goal gave them a target – and immediately I could see in their work, and indeed my own, a renewed vigour. So much so that when that time was up, the three of us came together, surveyed what we had done and more importantly what remained.

"We'd never live it down with my cousins if we left that bit behind. They'd be calling us city softies," I suggested.

It maybe took another 20 minutes as three of us found new energy to increase our rate of progress down the line. In the end there was one row left. We attacked it on three fronts – I was at the bottom of the field, the young lad in the middle and my wife from the road side.

## PAST

It was coming on time for home and we still had two full rows of work to turn and foot. My cousin told his mother that there was no way we could finish unless we worked straight through until dark.

My aunt agreed and said the first thing we should do was sit down and rest for five minutes. That was music to our ears and to our tired limbs.

Then out of her speckled blue bib, she produced a bag of bulls-eyes sweets. Our eyes opened in delight. She gave us two each and told us that we were no longer boys but young men the way we had kept pace with the men during the day.

Then she looked back down at the turf that was still to be footed. "Do you know what," she said. "We'll finish that bit of work in no time and we'll finish off the sweets on the way home. They'll taste all the better for us because we'll have finished out the job in front of us."

## PRESENT

My hands had begun to bleed with the constant attrition of the skin against the turf tops which felt like pebble dashing to the touch. The previous half hour was agony every time I touched a sod and I knew the cuts would hurt for a week or two afterwards.

Both my wife and son had the intelligence to wear gloves but it was something I couldn't do. The grown ups of my youth would laugh at people who ever wore gloves – even on the coldest day of the year and there was a part of me inside which honoured that unwritten rule.

Finally we finished the work and got off the bog as quickly as we could.

Stopping in the nearest Apple Green on the way back, I became something of a spectacle in the toilet as I winced every times the flow of water poured over my wounds.

By the time I rejoined the others, I had cleaned out the dirt from the new cracks in my hands but was in such suffering that I was unable to drive the car the rest of the way home.

## PAST

When we resumed we found it was no longer work

but a game we were playing. The turf was a toy to be put together and all we could think of was the sound of approval my aunt would shower on us when finished.

The journey home on the back of the grey Ferguson tractor with my uncle driving, my aunt sitting on one of the big grey mudguards and my cousin and I on the other was more a victory procession than a time to feel the agony of what we did.

And the sweets! Ah, yes. Has anything ever tasted so wonderful than my aunt's bulls-eyes as she told us we were the best young lads that ever stood in shoe leather.

## PRESENT

Thinking of her genius, I tried to do the same. Coming out of Apple Green I bought a packet of Wine Gums and Jelly Babies and some drinks.

With my wife driving and in the car with my youngest son, I returned laden down with those and other goodies.

"Let's have a party," I said as I sat into the front seat. 'Party time for the bog workers."

As we ate in virtual silence, the throbbing in my hands brought to mind the Seamus Heaney 'digging'. He said that between his finger and his thumb, the squat pen rest and he would dig with it.

With the state of my fingers and thumb, I wished I had followed his advice.

# 15

# The Last Day Of The Ploughman

*Ay, the horses trample, The harness jingles now;*
*No change though you lie under, The land you used*
*to plough*

**A. E. Housman, Poet – Is My Team Ploughing?**

**P**loughing was considered the poetry of land work on my father's farm. This was true particularly in the old ways when a man worked a team of horses to paint a green field brown as he put line after line of toil into the transformation of his soil.

There was no greater sense of ridicule among landowners than to see the creations of crooked drills in a farmer's field. And unfortunately as my father got older, that became our lot and it was with a certain relief to us when he got us involved in the procedure.

That relief was tinged with sadness because the power that my father possessed in those great shoulders of his had begun to dissipate as he approached his late sixties. Without realising it, or maybe realising it but without telling us, he had started to take shortcuts in how he tilled the land. With the crust hard to break in on our upland fields, it required plenty of grubbing and harrowing to prepare the topsoil for the plough.

When my mother died, my father made the supreme sacrifice of sending both of us to boarding school to give us the opportunity of a better quality of life than he had. I don't believe he felt there was anything wrong with his life on the farm; but he saw the rapid change from his ways to the more modern ones during the sixties and early seventies and felt our small holding could never sustain a family into the next generation.

The second last year of his life he did all the tilling work himself so that by the time we came home for holidays, the potatoes, the turnips and the mangolds were well in the ground. We had to take his word for that because there was so much scutch grass and weeds in our tillage field – that you couldn't be sure what crops had been sown or even where they were.

It meant a long, hot summer on our knees thinning the mangolds and turnips and weeding the stalks of the spuds to make sure they could grow.

Other years we would also till part of a big field down in Woodfield which was moor land. It was (almost) a pleasure to weed the crops down there because the cool, moist soil was soft on your hands and whatever weeds were in the drills would come away effortlessly when you wrapped your fingers around them.

This land, though, was a different proposition, it was stony brown soil, heavy to the hand and sharp and cutting to the touch. By the end of the first day's thinning, it felt like your nails and the soft part of your palms had been slashed with rapiers. It was virtually impossible to get the dirt out from under your nails despite several washings in the basin with carbolic soap and hot water.

There were times when, after finding a big round stone out the back, you'd just hold it in your hands to cool the semi-butchered areas which had gone 15-rounds with God's earth that day.

By the end of the first week, the hands would have hardened up but the knees and legs felt like they were about to seize-up. This was due to the way we rolled and tied old style jute bags around the knee area and kept them in place by tightly tying strings of binder-twine. Dragging yourself up and down a field hundreds of times on all fours is something the

Gestapo would have ruled out because of its degree of cruelty, especially when the work was overhung with hot and humid weather.

There was no hiding place during those gruelling weeks; the turnips and mangolds had to be thinned and besides, there was also the fact that our cousins had more acreage under the plough and seemed to be always ahead of us in their work.

It was while listening to the older people talking one Sunday evening that it dawned on me why our work was so much harder than theirs. My uncle wasn't the sort to say that my father hadn't done the ploughing preparations properly but by suggesting that my brother and I should step up to the mark to help him, he was letting us know there was a problem.

"You can't expect a man of his age to work with a horse all day long and do it properly," he explained. "No better man behind a plough than your father until the last few years." At moments and little talks like that, a great uneasiness descends. My uncle was being decent yet his innuendo couldn't be avoided.

"It's called the march of time, and it catches us all in the end," he added philosophically as he saw my countenance's reaction to what he had just uttered.

The following year we took on board his advice and attempted to move the goalposts slightly when it came to doing this work. My father had accepted in that year a lower standard in doing things which he would have laughed out of court when he had the strength of an ox inside his wide 5'10" frame.

My brother and I both took turns with the grubber and harrow and found that it was a merely a question of constantly going over the ground to get it fit for the first insertion of the point of the plough.

My father set up a square as a measurement by tapping pieces of wood into the ground and spooling twine down between headlands. He plumbed the ploughing area with a renewed meticulousness as if he had been embarrassed at his own lack of attention to detail in the previous year.

He liked to have two horses pulling the plough but this year he said the mare was so strong that she could do the work herself. 'Besides, for a big horse, she is very tidy the way she places her hooves," he said.

For half an hour, my brother and I watched spellbound as my father and the mare metamorphosed from man and horse into the one working being. He spoke, sotto vocce, to her every step as they set the first furrow, then he allowed the plough fall on its side when they reached the headland and walked to where he had pegged out for the return. As he gently nudged the reins, he spoke softly again to the mare to align her and the plough..

"Woh girl," he directed softly.

She stopped, her ears pricked in concentration and slowly stepped into where she was being gently directed. The singletree and the chains from her tacklings swung quietly like a rosary beads in the hands of a church worshipper.

"Easy," he coaxed, "easy". She obeyed by advancing with dainty steps to line herself up in the alley between the drills.

"Kind, girl, kind."

She followed as if on remote control.

"Good girl. And again."

She came in another step.

Then, holding his unlit pipe upside down in his mouth, he clicked his tongue on three occasions – telling her to pull ahead – as he quietly allowed the reins to fall on her back. She dug in her front hooves to power away like a sprinter exploding out of the blocks. Her back expanded as she found forward momentum and once she was up and moving, she looked as if pulling a plough came effortlessly to her.

The sock began lifting the terrain and my father subtly changed weight from one handle to the other behind her like a conductor to ensure the sod turned over evenly every foot of the way. The topsoil was being painted an even darker brown than the grubbed version in this mesmeric union of man, horse and plough in liberating the hidden earth.

There was something ceremonial and almost religious watching the ploughing in this old-fashioned method. Having completed four perfect channels of drills on either side, my father stopped for a rest.

"Get the mare a drink," he asked me, while he balanced against the plough to fill and light his pipe.

My brother asked him if he should take over so that my father could take a longer rest. He didn't answer. The mare drank lustily from the big bucket with all the water disappearing in one long inhalation. I was about to go for a refill when my father told me that she had had enough for the moment.

As he did so, he beckoned to my brother, in answer to his question, by telling him to take the reins. Using the drills already created as a guide, my brother ploughed a straight drill as if he had been doing it all his life. My father followed the new pairing of mare and eldest son like a wicketkeeper on guard in case of a mistake.

"A little left, good lad, use your hands to balance the plough, a small bit the other way. " He watched the pair make a perch (seven yards, then progress another two perches).

"Perfect," he said with a tone of approval.

"Great work."

My brother was fully concentrated, his feet jigged to keep the weight of the plough constant behind the mare's raw power and you could see the relief when he reached the other headland. Just as my father had done, he threw the handles of the plough to the ground so that it could slide without inserting its nose into the clay as he crossed over to the other side.

My brother and the mare worked in tandem for most of the afternoon. Now and again, my father would get up from his knee, put his pipe in his top waistcoat pocket and say proudly to him: "Take a break to rest your back, a mhic," and would take up the reins and get back into the groove.

All the while I ran the outfield lines, picking up the odd large stone, getting water for the mare and going home to get tea and sandwiches for the two workmen.

I had noticed on occasions before that sometimes when my father and brother worked together on a day such as that day, they became amazingly close. I was the outsider looking in.

I didn't feel jealousy at such moments – only a little regret that I was not as adroit at such work as my brother was. I was happy to witness something that was sacrosanct and in many ways traditional – a father handing down the tools of such noble work to his eldest son as had been done for him and previous generations in our family.

Standing there observing, it was easy to feel that there was something seamless in the ways of nature as we, the living followed that day in the footsteps of generations who had tilled that same field before but were long since dead.

Just as the furrows were narrowing into perfect

sonnets in the middle, my father and brother called me over. I assumed it was to run another errand as that had been my role up to then.

"Get your hands on the plough there now, a mhic," my father directed me. Then to my brother, he said: "Keep the mare in line, you, so that we plough out that last scrape as straight as a die."

I can only imagine how we looked in the tillage field on that day as the sun's rays cast long evening shadows across our work.

The two senior players were now giving me a moment's rite of passage as a ploughman and it was vital I held my nerve and kept the straight line of the previous furrows.

Under my father's careful guidance, nervously, I too danced the ploughman's shuffle as I leaned on the handles, first to one side, then the other, to keep its tilling eye on an even keel like a ship at sea. That's how I envisaged it as I looked at the sock turning over the earth. In my mind, the plough was a big boat gently breaking the sea swell with its bow.

All three of us followed the plough, my brother encouraging me, my father coaching me and ahead the mare benignly pulling me along.

The feeling of ecstasy I felt as I followed my father's advice to "plough out the whole headland" was perhaps what a player feels when scoring a winning goal in an All-Ireland.

As the mare veered right at the end in response

to my soft pull on the reins, I flung the handles of the plough to the ground, instantly feeling a tsunami of adrenaline which only coursed the inner being in rare and special moments.

All three of us, my father from a stooped position he was want to adopt to rest, my brother totally erect and smiling broadly at my achievement and myself, as I sat on my hunkers, were still on the upper headland.

This was the last moment of the ploughman's day and we looked across our work as if in meditation as our eyes retraced the steps we had taken up and down the field on this perfect tilling day.

Only the crows landing to scavenge on the newly overturned soil in search of food and the sound of the mare's long tongue tightening around the dew-filled tufts of fresh headland grass broke the silence.

The ploughed field was the poem we had just written, line by exact line, stanza by demanding stanza to the climactic creation we had penned in the clay with the last sweep of the plough.

For me and my brother, it was the end of our initiation as ploughmen; as it transpired, it was my father's final signature – a fitting epitaph in the soil for a man who loved such things.

# 16

# Shear
# Pleasure

There are times and things in life that are forever etched in memory like writing on a headstone – they may fade somewhat but they never vanish completely.

Farm life was about hardship and privilege in equal measure. The hardship was some of the work that had to be done like the thinning of the turnips, the pulling of buachaláns (ragworts), and the spreading of cow dung with a fork. A day's work under any of those disciplines made you feel that prisoners in jail for heinous crimes had a better quality of life than yours.

The privilege was being allowed a day off school

at harvest or turf time or maybe being grown up enough to use the paddy-rake behind the horse when bringing in hay. That was all work a young person could look forward to with real relish.

Sheep straddled both sections of the equation – taking maggots from lambs was one of the worst things we had to do on the farm but the day the sheep got sheared and the day you were brought to the next town to sell the wool were both highlights in any given year.

There was no free passage to anything under our regime. If you didn't sow with hard work, you didn't reap the rewards.

I knew this and with my brother away, I was given the chance on the day the man, with the same surname as ourselves, came to shear the sheep.

In fact, I was only following my cousin whose older brother was also away, which meant the two of us could play the lead roles in this important financial day in a farm's earnings. While the money was nowhere nearly as important as a milk cheque or the income from the sales of cattle, it provided a good contribution that my father, and my mother when she was alive, earmarked to buy clothes with for all of us.

It was tough work having to catch every sheep in both farms, guide them to the man with the shearing machine, pop them on their tail-ends for him and negotiate them in beside his right knee despite the sheep's constant wriggling to be set free.

The shearer himself had a red complexion from his work but his grip was vice-like. Once the ewe or lamb was caught in that strong arm of his, it had no choice but to sit back and enjoy the music of the old electric shears as it groaned and rattled the wool off its back.

As the day went on both my cousin and I became more expert at catching the sheeps' fleeces and learnt that the best way to avoid a wrestling match with each animal was to keep a firm pressing on them while they sat upright.

The animals were virtually powerless in this position and that in turn allowed us to take a break and examine close up how the shearer went about his work.

He was a man of few words; a nod towards us was his way of demanding the next ewe or lamb, then he would begin following his own left hand down the sheep's fleece as he expertly managed to take the coat of wool off in one fell swoop.

There were times when this wasn't possible; often sheep would have only part fleeces having been caught in bushes or if they suffered a bad case of maggots it badly affected the growth of wool afterwards.

The man worked from a spread-eagled gait as he used his legs and knees to nudge each sheep in the direction which would allow him to continue the seamless shearing of a fleece.

Every now and then he would stop for a drink, straighten himself up and say after surveying how many still had to be shorn: "We better get going again or we won't get finished by night."

At dinner-time around one o'clock, he would come in, sit at the bottom of the table and relish a meal of chops, cabbage and potatoes. He was precise in his eating habits and laconic in his conversation. Indeed, he was the sort of man who was respected because his silences carried as much if not more weight than his words.

You felt that while you were talking back to him, you were holding him up. My aunt didn't notice that as she spoke his eyes flickered from her to the clock behind her. No sooner had she drawn breath than he was reaching for his cap on his knee, standing up and thanking her profusely for the lovely meal.

There was a great rhythm in this work to the extent that when afternoon tea arrived, it felt like an intrusion. We ate and drank on the hoof, wiping the perspiration from our brows before touching the bread and butter.

All the while we were scurrying and running hither and thither, my father was on his knees carefully folding each fleece tightly one on top of the other.

By tea-time, we were finished – the sheep looked totally different running around in their version of underwear, bleating for their older lambs who had avoided the early session cull of the butchers.

My hands felt both oily from the wool and sore from the constant grabbing of the sheep fleeces during the day. Trying to milk the cows by hand afterwards was an agony as those same tired fingers had little strength left in them to do follow-on work.

But it was man's work you were asked to do – and by doing it you had graduated from boy to man on the farm ladder.

# 17

# Pulling
# The Wool

My father had a wool bag – a huge big jute container big enough for a boxer to spar, if not exactly fight in.

The wool was carefully placed in this container and put into the pony's cart for transport to the wool merchants in the next town five miles away. This was the trip away I had earned from the hard work I had put in on shearing day. The mesmeric clip-clop of the newly-shod pony's hooves on the roads was like a clock counting down the yards from our house to that other town. People waved as we drove past them, most saluting my father.

Then they would see the big wool bag and shout after us that we were in for a fine pay-day by the look of what we were transporting. I loved the whole 'feel' of this day; it was one of optimism and privilege.

My father was fond of the brothers he did business with on this journey; he said they would always treat him decently and paid him in cash. He preferred that to the rigmarole of a cheque, which then had to be lodged and cleared.

One of the men was particularly fond of my father and seeing him arrive at the gateway to his premises just beyond the river, came down to greet us.

"And that's a fine young man you have there. A cut of his uncles," he declared, much to my bemusement as I didn't know what such a remark meant seeing that all my uncles looked different to each other.

Still when he searched his pockets and a produced a tanner (an old sixpenny bit), I was all smiles, instantly calculating what I could buy with it to bring home.

We left the pony to drink and eat the grass at the side of the yard as we headed up the town, with the cash in my father's wallet, to buy clothes.

This first year when I accompanied him, we were delegated by my mother to buy a suit for my brother. Within a minute of walking into the shop, my father had spotted the one he wanted. The woman behind the counter was surprised at the swiftness of the purchase and also a little disconcerted that what he had bought might come back to haunt him when my mother saw it.

Intuitively, I had a similar feeling but my father wasn't the sort to spend a day pouring over different colours from Saville Row. To him a suit was a suit and that was the long and short of it.

"Let's go for a bite," he said to me as the woman in the shop enthusiastically tied up her sale in strong brown paper and twine.

The restaurant was nearby but obviously wasn't used to serving people at this time of day. When we asked if they were open, the bald man signalled for us to enter, showing us to a table covered in a red and white cloth.

There was a handwritten menu but very little of what was written down appeared to be on the premises. He was out of duck and chicken and he was also waiting for the fish to arrive from the Dublin market.

I was afraid my father would storm out in high dudgeon at this excuse for a menu but he ended up asking the man what he had that we could sink our teeth into. In the end we settled for soup and ham sandwiches but we had to wait for them.

The 30 minute delay between giving our order and our first sign of food was taken up by my father filling and lighting his pipe and then talking to me about how the wool had saved his family many years before.

It seems that during the time of the Black and Tans in Ireland there was the odd case around our town of a man being shot at who was on the run from them.

My father was only a young lad, probably in his middle teens, when the following incident occurred. Shortly after he himself and his mother had had a fierce set-to with the leader of the Tans in which my granny came out tops, they were presented with a tricky situation late one night.

With a curfew in operation, they were shocked out of their sleep by a loud knocking on the door. My granny answered the call without fear and my father could hear muffled whispers as she closed the front door to the night and brought the man into our kitchen. By the time my father had put on his trousers and alighted the stairs, his mother was directing the man towards the back door. Seeing my father enter the kitchen, she nodded at him to follow them to the outhouses.

On the pony's cart, the wool of that year was in the big jute bag cum container that had been handed down through the years. Working swiftly, she undid many of the fleeces, handing them to my father to put on the floor.

She then built up some of those fleeces around an empty centre before directing the man to cradle himself inside her hiding place. The man, who was holding a shoulder that appeared to have a bullet lodged in it, grimaced as she eased him inside her hastily constructed hiding place.

She then placed a small trailer creel over the man before directing my father to cover the top with the wool he had been directed by her to place on the floor. They then went back into the house and locked the back door behind them.

The man was a hero of my grandmother's family and she knew he probably had been on a mission against the Tans when he was wounded. She also knew that if she was found to be aiding and abetting him, she would suffer on the double for having had the temerity to not only cross him but defeat him in the eyes of the public.

My father and uncle had seen the leader march in the nude in one of our back-fields and shouted out 'halt' in fun. That night the leader came to take away my father, but didn't reckon on the strength of my grandmother and her threat to write to the king of England about his nude episode. The full story of how my granny took on the Black and Tans and won is contained in the first volume of these stories called *The Lie Of The Land*.

At first light the Tans began calling house to house to see if anyone had been in contact with what the leader termed 'a fugitive they were pursuing.' My granny, who my father claimed was incapable of telling a lie in normal circumstances, never flinched as she assured the officer no fugitive had darkened her door the previous night.

She later explained to my father that in her eyes,

the man wasn't a fugitive but a friend, so she hadn't told a lie.

She had my father put the harness on the pony shortly after the Tans left and yoked her to the cart on which the man, nestled in the giant bag of wool, was hidden away.

The mother and son set out for the next town in the early morning knowing that at the county border, roughly half-way on the journey, they would probably have to face up to a search of the cart.

As they set out, it had begun to rain and as both mounted the cart via the back creel, they brought another jute bag to act as a canopy over their heads on the way. My father said he could sense the apprehension in his mother's veins but she had a wonderful bravery about her. This man, she confided, as they drove on with the wool had blown up the Woodfield bridge beside our land and was being pursued with an unofficial death sentence on his head.

She was a woman without a man's guidance or back-up so she had to get through life with my father's man-boy assistance and her own courage and convictions that she was doing the right thing.

We waited what seemed like an eternity for the soup to arrive, though we could hear the noise of cooking activity of some sort coming from the kitchen. My father talked on as if he was that young person driving the pony and dreading the prospect of the potential frisking ahead.

"As it happened it rained cats and dogs and when we got to the border between the two counties, luckily there was no Tan presence; they must have retreated into their temporary dwellings for shelter," he explained.

"In fact," he went on as a faint blue breath of smoke exhaled from his nostrils from his pipe smoke, "we didn't see a sinner on that journey until we pulled up at the gate where you and I went in this morning. But if we thought we were out of the woods, we were very much mistaken.

"That Tan militia had regrouped into the town and as bad luck would have it, had just arrived in the wool merchants shortly before we turned up. They were searching through the material on the two levels of loft in the building and once they saw us enter the yard, two men came over to examine our load."

I heard my poor mother invoke: 'Jesus, Mary and Joseph' as she sought divine help before daintily alighting, taking off her glasses to dry them and greeting the quasi-soldiers with a warm voice.

"'Thanks for your help, lads,' she began, deliberately misrepresenting their authoritative approach as if they were coming to give her a hand. 'You have come to help us haven't you? We could do with it. It's taken us all our time to keep the wool dry on the way over with that downpour and the sooner we get it inside, the better.'"

At this stage the soup arrived and his narrative was momentarily interrupted. Both of us began eating the sandwiches and soup with great gusto, such was the hunger the delay and the anticipation of what might be presented, had aroused in us.

By the time the man came out with the pot of tea, we had emptied the bowls and eaten a round of sandwiches. After my father had poured the tea for both of us, he reclined a little further in the wooden chair and continued with his story.

"She was known to the Tans from that previous episode outside of our house and I'd suppose you'd say she was a marked woman. But your granny was also a very resourceful and clever person and must have reasoned that the best form of defence was to show total fearlessness in the face of the fear she was trying to contain.

"Her logic was that if you don't want someone to do something, almost invite them to do it. That was the best way to keep the hidden person from being exposed.

"So by asking them for help to carry the big bag of wool in, she was hoping they would decline. One or two of them took a step in her direction before their leader spoke.

"Calling 'halt' to his men, he told my mother that they weren't serving boys for either her or the premises they were on and suggested she get the owner and his son to help her.

"That was the opening my mother needed. Immediately she moved inside, calling the owner's name and telling him she needed his strength and that of his young lad, who was about the same age as me, to carry in the wool.

"For a second or two the pair exchanged a strange glance. 'Will you help me on my errand?' she asked with a little note of stiffness and desperation in her question.

"That's why we always come here," my father explained as an aside. "It's because of that man, God rest him – God rest my mother as well – for what he did for us that day.

"He knew instantly that she had encountered some sort of trouble. He directed his son to bring out a buggy on which to put the wool. He whispered something to his son as they negotiated the buggy alongside the cart.

The wool man was not particularly big but was strong and got me and his own young lad to lift the front of the wool bag while his massive arms grabbed the undercarriage to transfer it from the pony's cart to the buggy.

Just as he was about to lift, he asked the Black and Tan lads to bring my mother inside. "This isn't woman's work, lads," he said off-handedly. "Would you mind escorting her into my premises."

Whether this particular crew of 'Tans were used to jumping to order or whether the man's voice carried sufficient authority, two of the group stepped forward and did as they were bid.

While they went off with my mother, the wool man sped on his way to the ramp at the back before anyone could think to question him.

By the time we all went in through the main entrance in the way he had directed the Tans to take my mother, about a minute had elapsed.

The man had begun putting the wool fleeces into huge vat containers when we arrived. It was quite dark and he greeted with a hint of mischief in his voice.

"Lads," he chided gently, "would you all not have brought the lady into the kitchen for a cup of tea while I looked after business here?"

The captain of the 'Tans had enough at that stage and stepping forward, he ordered the wool man to stop what he was doing.

The others began searching through our bag and then the content of other vats around the old barn that was adjacent to the river.

As they did so, the wool man took my mother gently by the arm and directed her towards the waterfront.

With his left hand hidden from the view of the searching soldiers inside, he pointed into the reeds at the other side of the river. Later my mother said she could detect the slightest movement. It transpired that in the short time away from view with the wool man, the man who was hiding was released from his trap and directed into the water.

He stayed among the reeds for a number of hours before the man arranged to get him to safety after he had been treated by a doctor.

Every year, my mother returned with the wool and would always thank the man for how he had saved her friend's life.

In return, he would make my mother out to be the real heroine of the hour by declaring to whoever happened to be present with them – "Here's the woman who led the Black and Tans on a merry dance simply by pulling the wool over their eyes."

# 18

# The Last Day
# Of Summer

How many ways are there to describe the last day of summer? For some, it might be the 31st of July as the calendar says. For me, it was the day before I went back to school after the long summer holidays.

You broke up in early June after the internal exams – a little later if it was public exams – and the long months of summer ahead looked like a road with no ending.

The first night home from boarding school seemed like heaven – no more class or responsibility to study until...the last day of summer somehow arrived again and your mind was back into an impending outlook of sadness and doom and gloom.

It was like looking down a dark and bleak road into October and the winter months until December and especially the thoughts of Christmas would raise your spirits by allowing you to be free again.

Going back to school in January was less of a problem because it held out the promise of spring, longer days and the regrowth of another exciting season ahead for nature and for teenagers.

You had big signposts in your mind – St Patrick's Day and Easter, both of which allowed you to enjoy the passing days while waiting for the destination of the next big school holiday. The last term, even if Easter was early, was still the door to open up to the summer and three months away from the iron rations of boarding school food, the discipline of class and school and the isolation of being away from home and family.

All those feeling were magnified several times on that last day of summer. That September return posed the biggest problem to the psyche. The feeling of not being able to continue enjoying the familiar and maybe even the banality of day-to-day farm work and evenings of football or socialising.

As is always the case with youth, I only ever looked at this snapshot in time from my own perspective...until a neighbour came to visit my father and myself on this last day.

It had been a late year and my brother, myself and my father had worked manfully to have the hay in by the end of August. That's how late the farming season was with us because of the rain that had fallen during the summer. On the previous day, my brother had gone to Dublin to look for a flat or digs for his year ahead in university, leaving my father and myself and the mare to finish the last field.

Fortunately, this was a small piece of ground and by early afternoon, we had drawn in several of the cocks for the reek of hay we were making in one corner of the field. It was a simple way of farming done with the same equipment – a horse and chains – for generations before us on this same bit of meadow.

My father yoked-up the mare with the collar, harnesses and long chain which went over the back of the cock of hay.

The trick, as he told me a hundred times, if you wanted to get all the butt of the cock away was to use a fork lifting up the back and around the sides. That way when the mare pulled, the chains went right under the cock and it all came away as you dragged it over to the reek. My father would throw up the hay forkful by forkful to me and my job was to put the hay out to the edge, walk it into the reek and make sure it would not 'slip'.

There was more than a degree of architecture going on as if you didn't do this process, the reek could fall apart or come in to a head too quickly.

"You are too narrow on the left back side," my

father would direct after drawing in the next cock. "If you don't walk that out, it will take the water during the winter."

For variety, we would change jobs after a few hours and I would get the chance to stretch my legs away from the smothering dust that rose out of the hay while walking on the reek.

The pitfall of bringing in the cock was that if you weren't careful or if the mare was too giddy, the chains would not engage at the right level and she would walk away with the top half of the cock, leaving a big butt of hay which you would then have to fork in across the field.

That sometimes happened when I was younger and my brother, who was much more expert on such matters, allowed me do 'his job' – as he called it. By this time I was expert enough not to do such a thing which kept the work flowing at a steady pace.

However, it was with a great sense of delight when a car pulled up outside the gate and a priest I did not recognize came in across the field, patting the dogs on the head to mollify them.

I saluted him as I returned with the cock but my father was squinting as he tried to make out his outline as he approached.

"Have you another fork there and I'll row in?" he called out as he came nearer.

Recognising the voice, my father was unusually animated as he welcome his cousin from Dublin. The last time I had seen him I was no more than four. The pony had just given birth and we named her little colt after my father's cousin, who was then home from the missions in Africa.

According to my mother, I had 'put my foot in it' when he stayed with us on that previous occasion. We had raised a piglet in a tea-chest in the downstairs bedroom earlier that year and I can still see the perplexed look on his face when I asked him how he slept in "the pig's room," after he emerged for breakfast the following morning.

"God, but you are a happy chap," he said as he came towards me to shake my hand as I arrived at the reek with the latest cock of hay.

Initially he mistook me for my brother but then appeared genuinely surprised when my father said it was me. "You've grown up to be a big lad," he said warmly. "The last time I saw you was at the breakfast when I stayed with you many years ago."

Out of deference to the memory of my mother, I didn't mention 'the pig's room' but it was on the tip of my tongue to reprise the line and see if he too remembered his shock at being housed in a sty of some sort.

With only my father and myself down the fields for the day, we had decided to bring a flask of tea instead of lighting a fire and drumming up the kettle as we normally did.

Unusually for him, my father downed tools by

sticking his fork in the side of the reek, which had reached eight or nine feet in height by the time his cousin arrived. He told me to draw in the last half dozen cocks and deposit them at different spots around the reek while he and the priest sat down for a cup of tea.

I don't know for sure how close the two were but I am certain my father had total respect for a man of the collar and was very proud of having a clergyman and a missionary in the family.

They sat down on the jute bag he had spread out and both were locked in deep conversation as I brought in the remaining cocks of hay. When that was finished, I joined them for a cup of tea and a sandwich.

They talked and I listened as I ate. I now knew that we would not finished the reek that evening as my father would under no circumstances expect a priest home from hottest Africa to work with his bare hands on his field. Instead he filled his pipe, lit up and told me to run and herd the cattle and rise water for the bullocks in Gurteen.

That meant he would sit there and chat with the priest and having seen me off to the train the following morning, he would come back down to the field by himself and complete the reek.

I ran down the adjoining lane to count the cattle and was delighted when I saw the baths – into which we put the water from the well – were still half full.

The rains had been so constant that some of the blind drains had pools of water which made the task of rising huge volumes of it very much easier.

To assuage my guilt, I rose a few dozen bucketfuls and ran back up the field, thinking that if we managed to get home and finish the milking and other chores at a reasonable hour, I might get up to the football field or go down the town for a few hours before packing and preparing for the journey ahead.

The last day of summer was full of melancholy; no more herding or rising of water, or milking for the rest of that particular year.

By the time I got back to the hay field, the sun was hanging low in the west and the fine evening was starting to fade into a blur of indistinct outlines. I arrived back into the field with the dogs who had accompanied me barking with delight to see my father again.

My father and the priest rose as one off the old undercarpet and looked in my direction. The priest beamed a big, friendly smile and said I was a great help and my father would miss me for the rest of the time I was away.

My father gazed at the ground while the priest spoke again.

"He'll miss you lads but he's doing what your Mammy wanted. He's given you an education so you can have a better life than this."

I heard what he said but my concentration was totally on this slight figure of a 68 year old man who for the first time I saw was struggling to cope emotionally with his own last days of summer.

Shortly afterwards, the priest left to visit my aunt. My father told him he would call over later to see him before he left to go back to Dublin.

That evening on the way home, after we had watered and fed the mare and turned her loose to graze in that same field, we barely talked.

He lit his pipe again in the pony and cart and when I stole the odd glance to see how he was, his stare was beyond me and I thought longing for a different world. I felt that if my father could die there and then, he would gladly do it, because however long the evenings of the coming months were to me in school, they were longer and lonelier for him there on his own.

That night I cried into the few hollow sleeping hours that I only ever could encounter on the last night of summer – but this time they were for my father and maybe also for the recognition that his time on earth, like his missionary cousin, was totally devoted to elevating someone's else life at the expense of his own.

# 19

# The Day The Music Died

Without doubt, it was the day the music died for me; the evening my mother slipped finally into unconsciousness and as midnight approached went away from us.

It was so unlike her to steal anywhere that her stepping quietly into the long goodnight was unbelievable as far as I was concerned.

Even with cancer eating across her entire body, even with one leg already amputated to halt its spread "and in the clay" as she would sometimes say, and even in that constant pain that was only partly dulled by ever increasing doses of morphine from our local nurse, my mother only ever talked of the future with optimism coated words and visions.

That was her style – the eternal planner of a future no matter how poor the present moment might look like to her.

Only once, a short time before she died on August 18, 1968 at ten minutes to midnight, did she inhale the full realism of her situation. Then she called my father and the two of us, her sons to her bedside.

Her glasses slightly askew on her head, she spoke as if she was reading off an autocue to tell us she loved us and would look out for us when she crossed over the great divide.

Her only demand from my brother and I was that we would never drink – as the memories of the illness inflicted on her father's curse in life was something she literally brought with her to her deathbed.

I recall that sorry scene, listening to her as if she was Nyree Dawn-Porter in The Forsythe Saga. It wasn't real to my mind to hear such dramatic words so I pretended to myself that she was merely reciting the words of a play or a poem.

Deep down, and this I was sure of, I knew my mother would never die and leave me.

That feeling was challenged almost immediately as my father's eyes welled up. Not a man to overdo ostentatious affection, he took my mother's hand and in a declaration before God and man said he would gladly "sell ever acre of the farm if he could buy a cure for her." That statement was to me the greatest testament of love I've ever witnessed between a man and woman.

It was all the more authentic and remarkable given his whole marriage situation – he was a 48-year-old bachelor when his marriage was arranged with my mother. They had one thing in common before they met – she declared she wanted to be a nun but her pragmatic mother had instead used her secondary education to get her a job in the local post office; He told the parish priest and his mother than he wanted to be a priest, which couldn't happen because he was his widowed mother's eldest son and as such was indispensable to her around the farm.

By the time his arranged marriage with my mother was made, he had raised his six siblings with his mother and in the Ireland of the fifties, I neither know how their courtship or affection grew after the wedding was planned.

There were times as I grew up where he became worried and preoccupied about making ends meet for us in life, to the extent that my mother would be afraid to ask him for money to buy the groceries.

That may sound excessive in the present day but my father came from a subsistence farming background where any pound that was generated was made a prisoner of until it would only be prised away with good reason.

I remember getting seven old pounds for my First Communion and hiding the money in a small biscuit tin in a compartment at the top of my wardrobe.

Feeling her anxiety that asking him for money would end up in a row, I gave her the money and for two weeks there was no worries about buying biscuits or briquettes or stuff which was anathema to him as "a waste of money."

While what I've written in the previous few paragraphs could be seen to portray my father as a scrooge and a mean man, that was not the case. For sure, he didn't throw money around but he was of his time by adopting that approach. He believed that a fool and his money was easily parted and his generation got a feeling of security by having a few quid saved to call on for the rainy day.

That's why a cow losing a milking quarter or a pig, lamb or calf dying had a particular reaction in farm households. Everyone, mother, father and children felt those drawbacks and took part in a grieving process.

I think it is true to say that his worries sometimes got the better of him and he coped with these through bouts of silences that she found very disconcerting.

I became very conscious and sensitive to these and would always side with my mother by telling my father what I thought of him for not talking to her.

In hindsight, he could have smacked me and shut me up very quickly for being so interfering, yet he never did.

I know my motivation in doing this was to bring normality back into the house and I am also happy that I managed to do so on several occasions. I learned from those situations that sometimes the elephant in a room is only a mouse if there is someone to make people aware of why their worries are there in the first place.

If life is merely a dress rehearsal for what follows, then the day the music died has been my stage for 46 years now. Witnessing the way my father and mother said their goodbyes both sustains me and it eats me up at the same time.

It was indeed a powerful reminder that he understood how important love is but the shame was we never got to live with such completeness once she was committed to the earth in the Monastery Cemetery and didn't return to the lonely house with us.

Abraham Lincoln once said that he had learned one thing about life – that it goes on. To which I can only add – it sure does.

The senior football team played a championship match the day she died, the cinema had a Clint Eastwood western on the Sunday, she died of a Saturday night and the pubs opened and closed as they had always done every Sunday.

The world went on regardless as ours fell apart.

It was a salutary lesson to me as I withdrew into my own world to watch how the one outside was behaving.

In the hours and days, weeks and months, years and decades that followed, I could not but feel the greatest empathy for the neighbours and townspeople in the way they rallied around for the three of us, and indeed for others who later found themselves in the same predicament as we were in.

It's why I may put my head down to sleep in a county on the coast every night but my thoughts go back to my home town and the security I got from the people there in the middle of the country.

The feeling of belonging is what makes us all either happy or unhappy when it isn't the case. Despite being sent away to boarding school and then college and work, I have walked every road, spoken to every neighbour and live in a virtual creation of the town where I grew up in my head.

My aunt, who was the nearest thing possible to a twin to my mother although she was three years younger – would often pose a question down the years from the day the music died for her too: "How much different would it have turned out for us all if God hadn't taken you mother in her prime?"

The answer, of course, is that we will never know

or find out. What we all knew though was that first and foremost her death left the longest shadow in my life and that of my father and brother.

But that was just the start of it. I don't think her sister, my aunt, who lived up the road from us, ever really recovered and I think that her and my first cousins in that house would say they too lost a second mother with her passing.

Her soul was full of life poetry; she was religious but not overly so; she was serious but only to punctuate rests from the fun she loved to generate; she was happy lots of times but was also predisposed to worry about the habitual things that shouldn't be given the affirmation of a second thought.

That worry was the reason she developed her cancer. She fought it fiercely for three years and her tears on the day I first saw her with her leg amputated were in sympathy for my uneasiness instead of any self-pity.

In front of my other aunt, her youngest sister, in Meath where she had gone to recuperate from the operation, she cried as if she had let me down for having only one leg for the rest of her life.

I was eleven that day but seeing her level of sadness and upset, I grew up there and then and told her the best lie I could think of on the spot.

I explained to her that I had seen a documentary on the television the previous night – which I had – which said they could fix false legs so that you'd hardly know the person didn't have two real legs – which was the lie bit of my story.

She looked at me to see if I was serious and when I added that the walk was nearly perfect except for a little jerk movement, that was good enough for her.

"Well, then, we'll get one of those artificial legs and I'll be on me bike," she said with an immediate enthusiasm.

My uncle and aunt laughed at the bike reference and soon she joined in, wiping the tears from her face due to the laughter rather than sadness. That was my mother. She could coat any situation with the sweetest optimism and crying could mean happiness in her world.

She rallied for a time after that; then she had to go back to St Vincent's on St Stephen's Green in Dublin. I wasn't allowed in to visit her when I went up so my aunt would sneak me in for a few minutes and then tell me to go across to the Green and play with the ducks.

That was a real pleasure for me – seeing a city flock to this lovely place on the fine days I stayed there waiting for my aunt and my father to finish their visit and seek me out for the journey home.

We got a lift to and from Dublin with a neighbour who was a commercial traveller and by the time my mother came home for the last time, he had driven us up and down for over a year. It wasn't a straight journey though as he had clients to call on, which resulted in our veering off the main road to parts of county Meath on the way up and Kildare on the return home.

The journey, which now takes about 70 minutes, extended to five hours the way we had to go as we left our house just after nine in the morning and arrived after two in the afternoon. Then we had an hour or hour and a half to visit my mother before leaving at four and getting home around nine at night.

It meant that the cows sometimes were milked only once a day and herding was neglected – it's what happens when a family has to cope with a prolonged serious illness.

When news came that she was coming home, I was excited that the house would become a home again. While she was away in hospital, we were loaned out for meals and overnight sleeps as my father tried to juggle working on the farm with visits to Dublin.

No one else shared my excitement; my aunt was constantly in tears and my father was distant when I talked to him about her return.

The reality was she had come home to die – and the finality was deeply upsetting to the two adults closest to her. My happiness only exacerbated their pain as sometime soon I would have to be told the truth of her situation.

When she came home, she was delivered via a wheelchair straight to the downstairs bedroom. My friend's mother was a nurse and she came over the first night with her medicine and was a constant during the rest of the summer. She injected her with morphine to kill my mother's growing pain from the cancer which by that stage had ravaged her body.

My overriding memory of the days she had with us was her virtual allergy to noise. "Turn down the television," she would ask and we got used to turning it down completely as we sat through a silent-movie period.

During the days of summer the boys from all around would play matches on the green field which our house looked out on.

One day my mother asked me to go out and tell the boys to stop shouting as it was driving her mad.

Reluctantly, I approached one of the older lads and asked could they stop playing as it was upsetting my mother inside.

It was an outrageously unfair request to a group of lads on their summer holidays but I could hear my friend explaining to the others that my mother was close to death and they should finish the game.

That was something I was not aware of. In my innocence, I had known she had cancer but I never once felt she would die or be close to death, as he had put it. The fact that I quizzed my father about it that evening led to the last meeting among the four of us

– my mother in the bed, my father and my brother and I sitting around her.

That meeting heralded the beginning of a number of goodbyes my mother decided she wanted to do before it was too late.

Once those were done, she deteriorated rapidly and died on the Saturday night after I had gone to bed with my younger cousin as company beside me.

From the back room we could hear them saying the rosary but even then it didn't dawn on me that death was in the house. It needed my cousin – the daughter my mother never had – to come up and tell us amid her tears that my mother had just passed away.

I didn't cry then but got dressed and went down to partake in the prayers. Her eyes were closed but she seemed to be just as she had been while sleeping a lot over the previous few months.

I watched the blankets to see if they were going up and down rhythmically as was always the case when I sat in to mind her during the day.

This time, though, there was no movement – all was still.

After the priest had come and gone and the neighbours too, my brother, my cousin and myself slept together in the one bed in a room we normally didn't use at the back of the house.

On one of the walls, a painting hung of a woman

in a blue habit reposing at a wake. I was transfixed by it and by the time we turned off the light, I knew it would take over my thoughts for the rest of the night.

The painting haunted me until sometime much later when finally I fell off to sleep.

In the moment after my father woke us up the following morning, I stole another look at the face on the wall and somehow made myself believe that the night before had not happened. Yes, I had only dreamt she had died because of the painting.

I was about to take comfort in that bending of reality when my father brought in black ties to us. "We'll need to wear these to mass, lads," he said in a hushed tone.

I had my last head-butt at reality. "Is Mammy really dead?" I asked with an earnest hope that he would tell me last night hadn't happened.

"She's gone alright but don't worry, she'll be looking after us again, lads," he said, fighting back tears. "We're going down to the chapel now not to pray for her but to her. Get ready quick or we'll be late."

# Acknowledgements

I would like to thank my family and friends for all their help and encouragement in the writing of this book.

It is an undertaking that needs plenty of support and sometimes a timely reprimand to get the quill moving again.

To Joe Coyle for bringing out the essence of the stories in the visual presentation of the book's covers and pages.

To all the people from around my own place whose proximity contributed in some way through word or deed to the stories.

And to the memory of John B Keane, who is the father of this genre and a constant reminder of the great stories that are part of ordinary life.

# Also By The Author

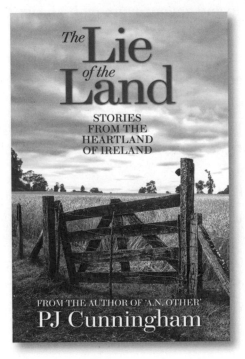

The 18 stories contained in PJ Cunningham's *The Lie Of The Land* mirror the challenges a not-too-distant generation of Irish people faced in their ordinary, everyday lives.

**His first book, *A.N. Other*, focused on rural life as seen through GAA activity in a parish.**

**Both books are available from Ballpoint Press, 4 Wyndham Park, Bray, Co Wicklow, Republic of Ireland. Telephone: 00353 86 8217631 Email: ballpointpress1@gmail.com Web: www.ballpointpress.ie**